The
Poetry of
Edward
Lear

The Poetry of Edward Lear

This edition published in 2019 by Arcturus Publishing Limited
26/27 Bickels Yard, 151–153 Bermondsey Street,
London SE1 3HA

AD006516UK

Printed in the UK

Contents

Introduction

Now regarded as one of the great English eccentrics of the Victoria era, Edward Lear has been variously described as a loner, an outsider, a man continually on the move, travelling throughout Europe, who eventually settled in Italy during the later years of an itinerant life.

Born in suburban London, in 1812, he was one of the 19, 20 or 21 children – depending on which biographer you believe – of Ann and Jeremiah Lear, a respectable middle-class family. There was nothing much to distinguish him from his brothers and sisters, except for his terrible eyesight, intermittent respiratory problems and a diagnosis of epilepsy at the age of five. Ann senior entrusted her eldest daughter, Ann junior, with bringing up the fragile and sickly Edward. She tutored him at home, nurturing the drawing and painting skills he showed at an early age and which she also possessed.

In 1828, the family moved away from London, but the odd couple remained, living in lodgings in Gray's Inn Road. Edward supported them by selling drawings and sketches, which attracted the attention of the Earl of Derby who wanted an artist to paint the animals at Knowsley, the Derby estate in Lancashire. Lear became a regular at Knowsley Hall between 1832 and 1837. The house, visited regularly by members of the aristocracy, was always full of children. Lear's charm made him a popular visitor. He loved the children, producing poems, drawings, alphabets and other 'nonsenses' for them, while charming their parents with conversation, his piano playing and the opportunity to buy his latest landscape paintings.

In 1837, ill-health forced him to leave Knowsley, and with the earl's patronage, he travelled to Rome to indulge his wish to be a painter of topographic landscapes in warmer climes. He stayed there for ten years, painting, writing poetry and making lifelong friendships. In 1846, he published some of his work, mostly limericks, illustrated by himself in a volume called *A Book of Nonsense*.

Jenny Uglow's biography identifies the next few years as those in which Lear most felt the pressures of being a gay man in the Victorian era. He travelled to Malta, Greece and France, often in the company of male friends. A restless spirit, he felt he was more able to pursue his 'dalliances' while away from England. None of this, however, prevented him from becoming a considerable figure in the mid-Victorian arts world, making friends with Alfred, Lord Tennyson and being invited to teach drawing to Queen Victoria.

Still on the move in his forties, he spent time travelling around the Mediterranean, India and Ceylon (now Sri Lanka), among other places. During these years, he had many long-distance friendships, but only two real companions: his manservant Giorgio Kokali from 1856 to 1883, and his cat Foss from 1871 to 1887.

In 1861, a new expanded edition of the *Book of Nonsense* was published. It was a huge success. He was delighted to receive such acclaim for what he thought of as something of a fun pastime. It encouraged him to write more complex poetry, which was published in three volumes during the 1870s after he had settled in a new home in San Remo, in Italy. The first of these included his most famous poems, 'The Owl and the Pussy-cat', 'The Dong with a Luminous Nose', 'The Duck and the Kangaroo', and 'The Jumblies'.

Edward Lear, the 'wandering nonsense minstrel', never completely free of either physical or emotional pain, contracted bronchitis in 1886. Unable to shake it off, he died at San Remo, in January 1888.

NONSENSE POEMS

The Owl and the Pussy-cat

I

The Owl and the Pussy-cat went to sea
In a beautiful pea-green boat,
They took some honey, and plenty of money,
Wrapped up in a five-pound note.
The Owl looked up to the stars above,
And sang to a small guitar,
'O lovely Pussy! O Pussy, my love,
What a beautiful Pussy you are,
You are,
You are!
What a beautiful Pussy you are!'

II

Pussy said to the Owl, 'You elegant fowl!
How charmingly sweet you sing!
O let us be married! too long we have tarried:
But what shall we do for a ring?'

They sailed away, for a year and a day,
To the land where the Bong-tree grows
And there in a wood a Piggy-wig stood,
With a ring at the end of his nose,
His nose,
His nose,
With a ring at the end of his nose.

III

'Dear pig, are you willing to sell for one shilling
Your ring?' Said the Piggy, 'I will.'
So they took it away, and were married next day
By the Turkey who lives on the hill.
They dined on mince, and slices of quince,
Which they ate with a runcible spoon;
And hand in hand, on the edge of the sand,
They danced by the light of the moon,
The moon,
The moon,
They danced by the light of the moon.

The Duck and the Kangaroo

I

Said the Duck to the Kangaroo,
    'Good gracious! how you hop!
Over the fields and the water too,
    As if you never would stop!
My life is a bore in this nasty pond,
And I long to go out in the world beyond!
    I wish I could hop like you!'
    Said the Duck to the Kangaroo.

II

'Please give me a ride on your back!'
    Said the Duck to the Kangaroo.
'I would sit quite still, and say nothing but 'Quack,'
    The whole of the long day through!

And we'd go to the Dee, and the Jelly Bo Lee,
Over the land, and over the sea; –
   Please take me a ride! O do!'
   Said the Duck to the Kangaroo.

III

Said the Kangaroo to the Duck,
   'This requires some little reflection;
Perhaps on the whole it might bring me luck,
   And there seems but one objection,
Which is, if you'll let me speak so bold,
Your feet are unpleasantly wet and cold,
And would probably give me the roo-
   matiz!' said the Kangaroo.

IV

Said the Duck, 'As I sate on the rocks,
   I have thought over that completely,
And I bought four pairs of worsted socks
   Which fit my web-feet neatly.
And to keep out the cold I've bought a cloak,
And every day a cigar I'll smoke,
   All to follow my own dear true
   Love of a Kangaroo!'

V

Said the Kangaroo, 'I'm ready!
   All in the moonlight pale;
But to balance me well, dear Duck, sit steady!
   And quite at the end of my tail!'
So away they went with a hop and a bound,

And they hopped the whole world three times round;
　　And who so happy, – O who,
　　As the Duck and the Kangaroo?

The Dong with a Luminous Nose

When awful darkness and silence reign
Over the great Gromboolian plain,
Through the long, long wintry nights; –
When the angry breakers roar
As they beat on the rocky shore; –
When Storm-clouds brood on the towering heights
Of the Hills of the Chankly Bore: –

Then, through the vast and gloomy dark,
There moves what seems a fiery spark,
A lonely spark with silvery rays
Piercing the coal-black night, –
A Meteor strange and bright: –
Hither and thither the vision strays,
A single lurid light.

Slowly it wander, – pauses, – creeps, –
Anon it sparkles, – flashes and leaps;
And ever as onward it gleaming goes
A light on the Bong-tree stems it throws.
And those who watch at that midnight hour
From Hall or Terrace, or lofty Tower,
Cry, as the wild light passes along, –
'The Dong! – the Dong!
The wandering Dong through the forest goes!
The Dong! the Dong!
The Dong with a luminous Nose!'

Long years ago
The Dong was happy and gay,
Till he fell in love with a Jumbly Girl
Who came to those shores one day.
For the Jumblies came in a sieve, they did, –
Landing at eve near the Zemmery Fidd
Where the Oblong Oysters grow,
And the rocks are smooth and gray.
And all the woods and the valleys rang
With the Chorus they daily and nightly sang, –
'Far and few, far and few,
Are the lands where the Jumblies live;
Their heads are green, and the hands are blue,
And they went to sea in a sieve.'

Happily, happily passed those days!
While the cheerful Jumblies staid;
They danced in circlets all night long,

To the plaintive pipe of the lively Dong,
In moonlight, shine, or shade.
For day and night he was always there
By the side of the Jumbly Girl so fair,
With her sky-blue hands, and her sea-green hair.
Till the morning came of that hateful day
When the Jumblies sailed in their sieve away,
And the Dong was left on the cruel shore
Gazing – gazing for evermore, –
Ever keeping his weary eyes on
That pea-green sail on the far horizon, –
Singing the Jumbly Chorus still
As he sate all day on the grassy hill, –
'*Far and few, far and few,*
Are the lands where the Jumblies live;
Their heads are green, and the hands are blue
And they went to sea in a sieve.'

But when the sun was low in the West,
The Dong arose and said;
– 'What little sense I once possessed
Has quite gone out of my head!' –
And since that day he wanders still
By lake and forest, marsh and hill,
Singing – 'O somewhere, in valley or plain
Might I find my Jumbly Girl again!
For ever I'll seek by lake and shore
Till I find my Jumbly Girl once more!'

Playing a pipe with silvery squeaks,
Since then his Jumbly Girl he seeks,
And because by night he could not see,
He gathered the bark of the Twangum Tree
On the flowery plain that grows.
And he wove him a wondrous Nose, –
A Nose as strange as a Nose could be!
Of vast proportions and painted red,
And tied with cords to the back of his head.
– In a hollow rounded space it ended
With a luminous Lamp within suspended,
All fenced about
With a bandage stout
To prevent the wind from blowing it out; –
And with holes all round to send the light,
In gleaming rays on the dismal night.

And now each night, and all night long,
Over those plains still roams the Dong;
And above the wail of the Chimp and Snipe
You may hear the squeak of his plaintive pipe
While ever he seeks, but seeks in vain
To meet with his Jumbly Girl again;
Lonely and wild – all night he goes, –
The Dong with a luminous Nose!
And all who watch at the midnight hour,
From Hall or Terrace, or lofty Tower,
Cry, as they trace the Meteor bright,
Moving along through the dreary night, –

'This is the hour when forth he goes,
The Dong with a luminous Nose!
Yonder – over the plain he goes;
He goes!
He goes;
The Dong with a luminous Nose!'

The Quangle Wangle's Hat

I

On the top of the Crumpetty Tree
    The Quangle Wangle sat,
But his face you could not see,
    On account of his Beaver Hat.
For his Hat was a hundred and two feet wide,
With ribbons and bibbons on every side
And bells, and buttons, and loops, and lace,
So that nobody ever could see the face
        Of the Quangle Wangle Quee.

II

The Quangle Wangle said
    To himself on the Crumpetty Tree, –
'Jam; and jelly; and bread;
    Are the best of food for me!

'But the longer I live on this Crumpetty Tree,
The plainer than ever it seems to me
That very few people come this way
And that life on the whole is far from gay!'
        Said the Quangle Wangle Quee.

III

But there came to the Crumpetty Tree,
    Mr and Mrs Canary;
And they said, – 'Did every you see
    Any spot so charmingly airy?
May we build a nest on your lovely Hat?
Mr Quangle Wangle, grant us that!
O please let us come and build a nest
Of whatever material suits you best,
        Mr Quangle Wangle Quee!'

IV

And besides, to the Crumpetty Tree
    Came the Stork, the Duck, and the Owl;
The Snail, and the Bumble-Bee,
    The Frog, and the Fimble Fowl;
(The Fimble Fowl, with a Corkscrew leg;)
And all of them said, – 'We humbly beg,
We may build out homes on your lovely Hat, –
Mr Quangle Wangle, grant us that!
        Mr Quangle Wangle Quee!'

V

And the Golden Grouse came there,
    And the Pobble who has no toes, –
And the small Olympian bear, –
    And the Dong with a luminous nose.
And the Blue Baboon, who played the Flute, –
And the Orient Calf from the Land of Tute, –
And the Attery Squash, and the Bisky Bat, –
All came and built on the lovely Hat
        Of the Quangle Wangle Quee.

VI

And the Quangle Wangle said
    To himself on the Crumpetty Tree, –
'When all these creatures move
    What a wonderful noise there'll be!'
And at night by the light of the Mulberry moon
They danced to the Flute of the Blue Baboon,
On the broad green leaves of the Crumpetty Tree,
And all were as happy as happy could be,
        With the Quangle Wangle Quee.

The Courtship of the Yonghy-Bonghy-Bò

I

On the Coast of Coromandel
Where the early pumpkins blow,
In the middle of the woods
  Lived the Yonghy-Bonghy-Bò.
Two old chairs, and half a candle, –
One old jug without a handle, –
  These were all his worldly goods:
  In the middle of the woods,
  These were all the worldly goods,
  Of the Yonghy-Bonghy-Bò,
  Of the Yonghy-Bonghy-Bò.

II

Once, among the Bong-trees walking
  Where the early pumpkins blow,
    To a little heap of stones
    Came the Yonghy-Bonghy-Bò.
There he heard a Lady talking,
To some milk-white Hens of Dorking, –
    ''Tis the lady Jingly Jones!
    On that little heap of stones
    Sits the Lady Jingly Jones!'
  Said the Yonghy-Bonghy-Bò,
  Said the Yonghy-Bonghy-Bò.

III

'Lady Jingly! Lady Jingly!
  Sitting where the pumpkins blow,
    Will you come and be my wife?'
  Said the Yonghy-Bonghy-Bò.
'I am tired of living singly, –
On this coast so wild and shingly, –
    I'm a-weary of my life:
    If you'll come and be my wife,
    Quite serene would be my life!' –
  Said the Yonghy-Bonghy-Bò,
  Said the Yonghy-Bonghy-Bò.

IV

'On this Coast of Coromandel,
  Shrimps and watercresses grow,
    Prawns are plentiful and cheap,'

Said the Yonghy-Bonghy-Bò.
'You shall have my chairs and candle,
And my jug without a handle! –
  Gaze upon the rolling deep
  (Fish is plentiful and cheap;)
  As the sea, my love is deep!'
Said the Yonghy-Bonghy-Bò,
Said the Yonghy-Bonghy-Bò.

V

Lady Jingly answered sadly,
  And her tears began to flow, –
  'Your proposal comes too late,
  Mr Yonghy-Bonghy-Bò!
I would be your wife most gladly!'
(Here she twirled her fingers madly,)
  But in England I've a mate!
  Yes! you've asked me far too late,
  For in England I've a mate,
  Mr Yonghy-Bonghy-Bò!
  Mr Yonghy-Bonghy-Bò!'

VI

'Mr Jones – (his name is Handel, –
  Handel Jones, Esquire, & Co.)
  Dorking fowls delights to send,
  Mr Yonghy-Bonghy-Bò!
Keep, oh! keep your chairs and candle,
And your jug without a handle, –
  I can merely be your friend!

– Should my Jones more Dorkings send,
    I will give you three, my friend!
  Mr Yonghy-Bonghy-Bò!
  Mr Yonghy-Bonghy-Bò!'

VII

'Though you've such a tiny body,
    And your head so large doth grow, –
        Though your hat may blow away,
    Mr Yonghy-Bonghy-Bò!
Though you're such a Hoddy Doddy –
Yet a wish that I could modi-
        fy the words I needs must say!
    Will you please to go away?
        That is all I have to say –
    Mr Yonghy-Bonghy-Bò!
    Mr Yonghy-Bonghy-Bò!'.

VIII

Down the slippery slopes of Myrtle,
    Where the early pumpkins blow,
        To the calm and silent sea
    Fled the Yonghy-Bonghy-Bò.
There, beyond the Bay of Gurtle,
Lay a large and lively Turtle, –
    'You're the Cove,' he said, 'for me;
        On your back beyond the sea,
    Turtle, you shall carry me!'
    Said the Yonghy-Bonghy-Bò,
    Said the Yonghy-Bonghy-Bò.

IX

Through the silent-roaring ocean
  Did the Turtle swiftly go;
    Holding fast upon his shell
  Rode the Yonghy-Bonghy-Bò.
With a sad primæval motion
Towards the sunset isles of Boshen
  Still the Turtle bore him well.
  Holding fast upon his shell,
    'Lady Jingly Jones, farewell!'
  Sang the Yonghy-Bonghy-Bò,
  Sang the Yonghy-Bonghy-Bò.

X

From the Coast of Coromandel,
  Did that Lady never go;
    On that heap of stones she mourns
  For the Yonghy-Bonghy-Bò.
On that Coast of Coromandel,
In his jug without a handle
  Still she weeps, and daily moans;
  On that little heap of stones
  To her Dorking Hens she moans,
  For the Yonghy-Bonghy-Bò,
  For the Yonghy-Bonghy-Bò.

Dingle Bank

He lived at Dingle Bank – he did; –
He lived at Dingle Bank;
And in his garden was one Quail,
Four tulips and a Tank:
And from his window he could see
The otion and the River Dee.

His house stood on a Cliff, – it did,
Its aspic it was cool;
And many thousand little boys
Resorted to his school,
Where if of progress they could boast
He gave them heaps of buttered toast.

But he grew rabid-wroth, he did,
If they neglected books,
And dragged them to adjacent cliffs
With beastly Button Hooks,
And there with fatuous glee he threw
Them down into the otion blue.

And in the sea they swam, they did, –
All playfully about,
And some eventually became
Sponges, or speckled trout: –
But Liverpool doth all bewail
Their Fate; – likewise his Garden Quail.

The New Vestments

There lived an Old Man in the Kingdom of Tess,
Who invented a purely original dress;
And when it was perfectly made and complete,
He opened the door, and walked into the street.

By way of a hat, he'd a loaf of Brown Bread,
In the middle of which he inserted his head; –
His Shirt was made up of no end of dead Mice,
The warmth of whose skins was quite fluffy and nice; –
His Drawers were of Rabbit-skins; – so were his shoes;–
His Stockings were skins, – but it is not known whose; –
His Waistcoat and Trowsers were made of Pork Chops; –
His Buttons were Jujubes, and Chocolate Drops; –
His Coat was all Pancakes with Jam for a border,
And a girdle of Biscuits to keep it in order;
And he wore over all, as a screen from bad weather,
A Cloak of green Cabbage-leaves stitched all together.

He had walked a short way, when he heard a great noise,
Of all sorts of Beasticles, Birdlings, and Boys; –
And from every long street and dark lane in the town
Beasts, Birdles, and Boys in a tumult rushed down.
Two Cows and a c alf ate his Cabbage-leaf Cloak; –
Four Apes seized his Girdle, which vanished like smoke; –
Three Kids ate up half of his Pancaky Coat, –
And the tails were devour'd by an ancient He Goat; –
An army of Dogs in a twinkling tore up his
Pork Waistcoat and Trowsers to give to their Puppies; –

And while they were growling, and mumbling the
    Chops,
Ten boys prigged the Jujubes and Chocolate Drops. –
He tried to run back to his house, but in vain,
Four Scores of fat Pigs came again and again; –
They rushed out of stables and hovels and doors, –
They tore off his stockings, his shoes, and his drawers; –
And now from the housetops with screechings descend,
Striped, spotted, white, black, and gray Cats without end,
They jumped on his shoulders and knocked off his hat, –
When Crows, Ducks, and Hens made a mincemeat of
    that; –
They speedily flew at his sleeves in trice,
And utterly tore up his Shirt of dead Mice; –
They swallowed the last of his Shirt with a squall, –
Whereon he ran home with no clothes on at all.

And he said to himself as he bolted the door,
'I will not wear a similar dress any more,
'Any more, any more, any more, never more!'

The Jumblies

I

They went to sea in a Sieve, they did,
In a Sieve they went to sea:
In spite of all their friends could say,
On a winter's morn, on a stormy day,
In a Sieve they went to sea!
And when the Sieve turned round and round,
And every one cried, 'You'll all be drowned!'
They called aloud, 'Our Sieve ain't big,
But we don't care a button! we don't care a fig!
In a Sieve we'll go to sea!'
Far and few, far and few,
Are the lands where the Jumblies live;
Their heads are green, and their hands are blue,
And they went to sea in a Sieve.

II

They sailed away in a Sieve, they did,
In a Sieve they sailed so fast,
With only a beautiful pea-green veil
Tied with a riband by way of a sail,
To a small tobacco-pipe mast;
And every one said, who saw them go,
'O won't they be soon upset, you know!
For the sky is dark, and the voyage is long,
And happen what may, it's extremely wrong
In a Sieve to sail so fast!'
Far and few, far and few,
Are the lands where the Jumblies live;
Their heads are green, and their hands are blue,
And they went to sea in a Sieve.

III

The water it soon came in, it did,
The water it soon came in;
So to keep them dry, they wrapped their feet
In a pinky paper all folded neat,
And they fastened it down with a pin.
And they passed the night in a crockery-jar,
And each of them said, 'How wise we are!
Though the sky be dark, and the voyage be long,
Yet we never can think we were rash or wrong,
While round in our Sieve we spin!'
Far and few, far and few,
Are the lands where the Jumblies live;
Their heads are green, and their hands are blue,
And they went to sea in a Sieve.

IV

And all night long they sailed away;
And when the sun went down,
They whistled and warbled a moony song
To the echoing sound of a coppery gong,
In the shade of the mountains brown.
'O Timballoo! How happy we are,
When we live in a Sieve and a crockery-jar,
And all night long in the moonlight pale,
We sail away with a pea-green sail,
In the shade of the mountains brown!
Far and few, far and few,
Are the lands where the Jumblies live;
Their heads are green, and their hands are blue,
And they went to sea in a Sieve.

V

They sailed to the Western Sea, they did,
To a land all covered with trees,
And they bought an Owl, and a useful Cart,
And a pound of Rice, and a Cranberry Tart,
And a hive of silvery Bees.
And they bought a Pig, and some green Jack-daws,
And a lovely Monkey with lollipop paws,
And forty bottles of Ring-Bo-Ree,
And no end of Stilton Cheese.
Far and few, far and few,
Are the lands where the Jumblies live;
Their heads are green, and their hands are blue,
And they went to sea in a Sieve.

VI

And in twenty years they all came back,
In twenty years or more,
And every one said, 'How tall they've grown!'
For they've been to the Lakes, and the Terrible Zone,
And the hills of the Chankly Bore!
And they drank their health, and gave them a feast
Of dumplings made of beautiful yeast;
And every one said, 'If we only live,
We too will go to sea in a Sieve,
To the hills of the Chankly Bore!
Far and few, far and few,
Are the lands where the Jumblies live;
Their heads are green, and their hands are blue,
And they went to sea in a Sieve.

The Daddy Long-Legs and the Fly

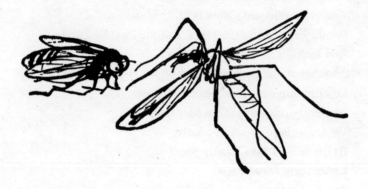

I

Once Mr Daddy Long-legs,
Dressed in brown and gray,
Walked about upon the sands
Upon a summer's day;
And there among the pebbles,
When the wind was rather cold,
He met with Mr Floppy Fly,
All dressed in blue and gold.
And, as it was too soon to dine,
They drank some Periwinkle-wine,
And played an hour or two, or more,
At battlecock and shuttledore.

II

Said Mr Daddy Long-legs
To Mr Floppy Fly,
'Why do you never come to court?

I wish you 'd tell me why.
All gold and shine, in dress so fine,
You'd quite delight the court.
Why do you never go at all?
I really think you *ought*.
And, if you went, you'd see such sights!
Such rugs! and jugs! and candle-lights!
And more than all, the King and Queen,
One in red, and one in green.'

III
'O Mr Daddy Long-legs!'
Said Mr Floppy Fly,
'It's true I never go to court;
And I will tell you why.
If I had six long legs like yours,
At once I'd go to court;
But, oh! I can't, because *my* legs
Are so extremely short.
And I'm afraid the King and Queen
(One in red, and one in green)
Would say aloud, 'You are not fit,
You Fly, to come to court a bit!"

IV
'Oh, Mr Daddy Long-legs!'
Said Mr Floppy Fly,
'I wish you'd sing one little song,
One mumbian melody!
You used to sing so awful well
In former days gone by,

But now you never sing at all;
I wish you'd tell me why:
For, if you would, the silvery sound
Would please the shrimps and cockles round,
And all the crabs would gladly come
To hear you sing, 'Ah, Hum di Hum!"

V

Said Mr Daddy Long-legs,
'I can never sing again!
And, if you wish, I'll tell you why,
Although it gives me pain.
For years I cannot hum a bit,
Or sing the smallest song;
And this the dreadful reason is, –
My legs are grown too long!
My six long legs, all here and there,
Oppress my bosom with despair;
And, if I stand or lie or sit,
I cannot sing one single bit!'

VI

So Mr Daddy Long-legs
And Mr Floppy Fly
Sat down in silence by the sea,
And gazed upon the sky.
They said, 'This is a dreadful thing!
The world has all gone wrong,
Since one has legs too short by half,
The other much too long!
One never more can go to court,

Because his legs have grown too short;
The other cannot sing a song,
Because his legs have grown too long!'

VII
Then Mr Daddy Long-legs
And Mr Floppy Fly
Rushed downward to the foamy sea
With one sponge-taneous cry:
And there they found a little boat,
Whose sails were pink and gray;
And off they sailed among the waves,
Far, and far away:
They sailed across the silent main,
And reached the great Gromboolian plain;
And there they play forevermore
At battlecock and shuttledore.

The Nutcrackers and the Sugar-Tongs

I

The Nutcrackers sate by a plate on the table,
The Sugar-tongs sate by a plate at his side;
And the Nutcrackers said, 'Don't you wish we were able
Along the blue hills and green meadows to ride?
Must we drag on this stupid existence for ever,
So idle and weary, so full of remorse, –
While every one else takes his pleasure, and never
Seems happy unless he is riding a horse?

II

'Don't you think we could ride without being instructed?
Without any saddle or bridle or spur?
Our legs are so long, and so aptly constructed,
I'm sure that an accident could not occur.
Let us all of a sudden hop down from the table,
And hustle downstairs, and each jump on a horse!

Shall we try? Shall we go? Do you think we are able?'
The Sugar-tongs answered distinctly, 'Of course!'

III

So down the long staircase they hopped in a minute,
The Sugar-tongs snapped, and the Crackers said 'Crack!'
The stable was open, the horses were in it;
Each took out a pony, and jumped on his back.
The Cat in a fright scrambled out of the doorway,
The Mice tumbled out of a bundle of hay;
The brown and white Rats, and the black ones from
    Norway,
Screamed out, 'They are taking the horses away!'

IV

The whole of the household was filled with amazement,
The Cups and the Saucers danced madly about,
The Plates and the Dishes looked out of the casement,
The Salt-cellar stood on his head with a shout,
The Spoons, with a clatter, looked out of the lattice,
The Mustard-pot climbed up the gooseberry-pies,
The Soup-ladle peeped through a heap of Veal Patties,
And squeaked with a ladle-like scream of surprise.

V

The Frying-pan said, 'It's an awful delusion!'
The Tea-kettle hissed, and grew black in the face;
And they all rushed downstairs in the wildest confusion,
To see the great Nutcracker–Sugar-tong race.
And out of the stable, with screamings and laughter,

(Their ponies were cream-colored, speckled with brown),
The Nutcrackers first, and the Sugar-tongs after,
Rode all round the yard, and then all round the town.

VI

They rode through the street, and they rode by the station,
They galloped away to the beautiful shore;
In silence they rode, and 'made no observation,'
Save this: 'We will never go back any more!'
And still you might hear, till they rode out of hearing,
The Sugar-tongs snap, and the Crackers say 'crack!'
Till far in the distance their forms disappearing,
They faded away. – And they never came back!

Calico Pie

I

Calico Pie,
The little birds fly
Down to the calico tree:
Their wings were blue,
And they sang 'Tilly-loo!'
Till away they flew, –
And they never came back to me!
They never came back!
They never came back!
They never came back to me!

II

Calico Jam,
The little Fish swam,
Over the syllabub sea.
He took off his hat
To the Sole and the Sprat,
And the Willeby-wat, –
But he never came back to me!
He never came back!
He never came back!
He never came back to me!

III

Calico Ban,
The little Mice ran
To be ready in time for tea,

Flippity flup,
They drank it all up,
And danced in the cup, –
But they never came back to me!
They never came back!
They never came back!
They never came back to me!

IV
Calico Drum,
The Grasshoppers come,
The Butterfly, Beetle, and Bee,
Over the ground,
Around and round,
With a hop and a bound, –
But they never came back!
They never came back!
They never came back!
They never came back to me!

Mr and Mrs Spikky Sparrow

I

On a little piece of wood,
Mr Spikky Sparrow stood;
Mrs Sparrow sate close by,
A-making of an insect pie
For her little children five,
In the nest and all alive;
Singing with a cheerful smile
To amuse them all the while,
Twikky wikky wikky wee,
Wikky bikky twikky tee,
Spikky bikky bee!

II

Mrs Spikky Sparrow said,
'Spikky, Darling! in my head
Many thoughts of trouble come,
Like to flies upon a plum!

All last night, among the trees,
I heard you cough, I heard you sneeze;
And thought I, It's come to that
Because he does not wear a hat!
Chippy wippy sikky tee,
Bikky wikky tikky mee,
Spikky chippy wee!

III

'Not that you are growing old;
But the nights are growing cold.
No one stays out all night long
Without a hat: I'm sure it's wrong!'
Mr Spikky said, 'How kind,
Dear! you are, to speak your mind!
All your life I wish you luck!
You are! you are! a lovely duck!
Witchy witchy witchy wee,
Twitchy witchy witchy bee,
Tikky tikky tee!

IV

'I was also sad, and thinking,
When one day I saw you winking,
And I heard you sniffle-snuffle,
And I saw your feathers ruffle:
To myself I sadly said,
She's neuralgia in her head!
That dear head has nothing on it!
Ought she not to wear a bonnet?'

Witchy kitchy kitchy wee,
Spikky wikky mikky bee,
Chippy wippy chee!

V

'Let us both fly up to town:
There I'll buy you such a gown!
Which, completely in the fashion,
You shall tie a sky-blue sash on;
And a pair of slippers neat
To fit your darling little feet,
So that you will look and feel
Quite galloobious and genteel.
Jikky wikky bikky see,
Chicky bikky wikky bee,
Twicky witchy wee!'

VI

So they both to London went,
Alighting on the Monument,
Whence they flew down swiftly – pop!
Into Moses' wholesale shop;
There they bought a hat and bonnet,
And a gown with spots upon it,
A satin sash of Cloxam blue,
And a pair of slippers too.
Zikky wikky mikky bee,
Witchy witchy mitchy kee,
Sikky tikky wee!

VII

Then, when so completely dressed,
Back they flew, and reached their nest.
Their children cried, 'O Ma and Pa!
How truly beautiful you are!'
Said they, 'We trust that cold or pain
We shall never feel again!
While, perched on tree or house or steeple,
We now shall look like other people.
Witchy witchy witchy wee,
Twikky mikky bikky bee,
Zikky sikky tee!'

The Broom, the Shovel, the Poker and the Tongs

I

The Broom and the Shovel, the Poker and Tongs,
They all took a drive in the Park;
And they each sang a song, Ding-a-dong, Ding-a-dong!
Before they went back in the dark.
Mr Poker he sate quite upright in the coach;
Mr Tongs made a clatter and clash;
Miss Shovel was dressed all in black (with a brooch);
Mrs Broom was in blue (with a sash).
Ding-a-dong, ding-a-dong!
And they all sang a song!

II

'O Shovely so lovely!' the Poker he sang,
'You have perfectly conquered my heart.
Ding-a-dong, Ding-a-dong! If you're pleased with
    my song,

I will feed you with cold apple-tart!
When you scrape up the coals with a delicate sound,
You enrapture my life with delight!
Your nose is so shiny! your head is so round!
And your shape is so slender and bright!
Ding-a-dong, Ding-a-dong!
Ain't you pleased with my song?'

III

'Alas! Mrs Broom,' sighed the Tongs in his song,
'Oh! is it because I'm so thin,
And my legs are so long, – Ding-a-dong, ding-a-dong!
That you don't care about me a pin?
Ah! fairest of creatures, when sweeping the room,
Ah! why don't you heed my complaint?
Must you needs be so cruel, you beautiful Broom,
Because you are covered with paint?
Ding-a-dong, Ding-a-dong!
You are certainly wrong!'

IV

Mrs Broom and Miss Shovel together they sang,
'What nonsense you're singing to-day!'
Said the Shovel, 'I'll certainly hit you a bang!'
Said the Broom, 'And I'll sweep you away!'
'So the Coachman drove homeward as fast as he could,
Perceiving their anger with pain;
But they put on the kettle, and little by little,
They all became happy again.
Ding-a-dong, Ding-a-dong!
There's an end of my song!

The Table and the Chair

I

Said the Table to the Chair,
'You can hardly be aware
How I suffer from the heat
And from chilblains on my feet.
If we took a little walk,
We might have a little talk;
Pray let us take the air!'
Said the Table to the Chair.

II

Said the Chair unto the Table,
'Now, you *know* we are not able:
How foolishly you talk,
When you know we *cannot* walk!'
Said the Table with a sigh,
'It can do no harm to try.
I've as many legs as you:
Why can't we walk on two?'

III

So they both went slowly down,
And walked about the town
With a cheerful bumpy sound
As they toddled round and round.
And everybody cried,
As they hastened to their side,
'See! the Table and the Chair
Have come out to take the air!'

IV

But in going down an alley,
To a castle in a valley,
They completely lost their way,
And wandered all the day;
Till, to see them safely back,
They paid a Ducky-quack,
And a Beetle, and a Mouse,
Who took them to their house.

V

Then they whispered to each other,
'O delightful little brother,
What a lovely walk we've taken!
Let us dine on Beans and Bacon.'
So the Ducky and the leetle
Browny-Mousy and the Beetle
Dined, and danced upon their heads
Till they toddled to their beds.

The Two Old Bachelors

Two old Bachelors were living in one house;
One caught a Muffin, the other caught a Mouse.
Said he who caught the Muffin to him who caught the
    Mouse, –
'This happens just in time! For we've nothing in the house,
Save a tiny slice of lemon and a teaspoonful of honey,
And what to do for dinner – since we haven't any
    money?
And what can we expect if we haven't any dinner,
But to lose our teeth and eyelashes and keep on growing
    thinner?'

Said he who caught the Mouse to him who caught the
    Muffin, –
'We might cook this little Mouse, if we only had some
    Stuffin'!

If we had but Sage and Onion we could do extremely well;
But how to get that Stuffin' it is difficult to tell!'

Those two old Bachelors ran quickly to the town
And asked for Sage and Onion as they wandered up and
      down;
They borrowed two large Onions, but no Sage was to be
      found
In the Shops, or in the Market, or in all the Gardens round.

But some one said, 'A hill there is, a little to the north,
And to its purpledicular top a narrow way leads forth;
And there among the rugged rocks abides an ancient
      Sage, –
An earnest Man, who reads all day a most perplexing page.

Climb up, and seize him by the toes, – all studious as he
      sits, –
And pull him down, and chop him into endless little bits!
Then mix him with your Onion (cut up likewise into
      Scraps), –
When your Stuffin' will be ready, and very good –
      perhaps.'

Those two old Bachelors without loss of time
The nearly purpledicular crags at once began to climb;
And at the top, among the rocks, all seated in a nook,
They saw that Sage a-reading of a most enormous book.
'You earnest Sage!' aloud they cried, 'your book you've
      read enough in!
We wish to chop you into bits to mix you into Stuffin'!'

But that old Sage looked calmly up, and with his awful book,
At those two Bachelors' bald heads a certain aim he took;
And over crag and precipice they rolled promiscuous
    down, –
At once they rolled, and never stopped in lane or field or
    town;
And when they reached their house, they found (besides
    their want of Stuffin'),
The Mouse had fled – and, previously, had eaten up the
    Muffin.
They left their home in silence by the once convivial door;
And from that hour those Bachelors were never heard of
    more.

The Pelican Chorus

King and Queen of the Pelicans we;
No other Birds so grand we see!
None but we have feet like fins!
With lovely leathery throats and chins!
Ploffskin, Pluffskin, Pelican jee!
We think no Birds so happy as we!
Plumpskin, Ploshkin, Pelican jill!
We think so then, and we thought so still

We live on the Nile. The Nile we love.
By night we sleep on the cliffs above;
By day we fish, and at eve we stand
On long bare islands of yellow sand.
And when the sun sinks slowly down
And the great rock walls grow dark and brown,

Where the purple river rolls fast and dim
And the Ivory Ibis starlike skim,
Wing to wing we dance around, –
Stamping our feet with a flumpy sound,
Opening our mouths as Pelicans ought;
And this is the song we nightly snort, –
Ploffskin, Pluffskin, Pelican jee!
We think no Birds so happy as we!
Plumpskin, Ploshkin, Pelican jill!
We think so then, and we thought so still!

Last year came out our Daughter Dell;
And all the Birds received her well.
To do her honour a feast we made
For every bird that can swim or wade, –
Herons and Gulls, and Cormorants black,
Cranes, and Flamingos with scarlet back,
Plovers and Storks, and Geese in clouds,
Swans and Dilberry Ducks in crowds:
Thousands of Birds in wondrous flight!
They ate and drank and danced all night,
And echoing back from the rocks you heard
Multitude-echoes from Bird and Bird, –
Ploffskin, Pluffskin, Pelican jee!
We think no Birds so happy as we!
Plumpskin, Ploshkin, Pelican jill!
We think so then, and we thought so still!

Yes, they came; and among the rest
The King of the Cranes all grandly dressed.
Such a lovely tail! Its feathers float

Between the ends of his blue dress-coat;
With pea-green trowsers all so neat,
And a delicate frill to hide his feet, –
(For though no one speaks of it, every one knows
He has got no webs between his toes).

As soon as he saw our Daughter Dell,
In violent love that Crane King fell, –
On seeing her waddling form so fair,
With a wreath of shrimps in her short white hair.
And before the end of the next long day
Our Dell had given her heart away;
For the King of the Cranes had won that heart,
With a Crocodile's egg and a large fish-tart.
She vowed to marry the King of the Cranes,
Leaving the Nile for stranger plains;
And away they flew in a gathering crowd
Of endless birds in a lengthening cloud.
Ploffskin, Pluffskin, Pelican jee!
We think no Birds so happy as we!
Plumpskin, Ploshkin, Pelican jill!
We think so then, and we thought so still!

And far away in the twilight sky,
We heard them singing a lessening cry, –
Farther and farther, till out of sight,
And we stood alone in the silent night!
Often since, in the nights of June,
We sit on the sand and watch the moon, –
She has gone to the great Gromboolian plain,
And we probably never shall meet again!

Oft, in the long still nights of June,
We sit on the rocks and watch the moon, –
She dwells by the streams of the Chankly Bore,
And we probably never shall see her more.
Ploffskin, Pluffskin, Pelican jee!
We think no Birds so happy as we!
Plumpskin, Ploshkin, Pelican jill!
We think so then, and we thought so still!

The Pobble Who Has No Toes

I

The Pobble who has no toes
Had once as many as we;
When they said, 'Some day you may lose them all;'
He replied, 'Fish fiddle de-dee!'
And his Aunt Jobiska made him drink
Lavender water tinged with pink;
For she said, 'The World in general knows
There's nothing so good for a Pobble's toes!'

II

The Pobble who has no toes,
Swam across the Bristol Channel;
But before he set out he wrapped his nose
In a piece of scarlet flannel.

For his Aunt Jobiska said, 'No harm
Can come to his toes if his nose is warm;
And it's perfectly known that a Pobble's toes
Are safe – provided he minds his nose.'

III

The Pobble swam fast and well,
And when boats or ships came near him,
He tinkledy-binkledy-winkled a bell,
So that all the world could hear him.
And all the Sailors and Admirals cried,
When they saw him nearing the further side, –
'He has gone to fish, for his Aunt Jobiska's
Runcible Cat with crimson whiskers!'

IV

But before he touched the shore,
The shore of the Bristol Channel,
A sea-green Porpoise carried away
His wrapper of scarlet flannel.
And when he came to observe his feet,
Formerly garnished with toes so neat,
His face at once became forlorn
On perceiving that all his toes were gone!

V

And nobody ever knew,
From that dark day to the present,
Whoso had taken the Pobble's toes,
In a manner so far from pleasant.
Whether the shrimps or crawfish gray,

Or crafty Mermaids stole them away, –
Nobody knew; and nobody knows
How the Pobble was robbed of his twice five toes!

VI

The Pobble who has no toes
Was placed in a friendly Bark,
And they rowed him back, and carried him up
To his Aunt Jobiska's Park.
And she made him a feast, at his earnest wish
Of eggs and buttercups fried with fish; –
And she said, – 'It's a fact the whole world knows,
That Pobbles are happier without their toes.'

Mr and Mrs Discobbolos

I

Mr and Mrs Discobbolos
Climbed to the top of a wall.
And they sate to watch the sunset sky,
And to hear the Nupiter Piffkin cry,
And the Biscuit Buffalo call.
They took up a roll and some Camomile tea,
And both were as happy as happy could be,
Till Mrs Discobbolos said, –
'Oh! W! X! Y! Z!
It has just come into my head,
Suppose we should happen to fall!!!!
Darling Mr Discobbolos!'

II

'Suppose we should fall down flumpetty,
Just like pieces of stone!
On to the thorns, or into the moat!
What would become of your new green coat?
And might you not break a bone?
It never occurred to me before,
That perhaps we shall never go down any more!'
And Mrs Discobbolos said,
'Oh! W! X! Y! Z!
What put it into your head
To climb up this wall – my own
Darling Mr Discobbolos?'

III

Mr Discobbolos answered, –
'At first it gave me pain, –
And I felt my ears turn perfectly pink
When your exclamation made me think
We might never get down again!
But now I believe it is wiser far
To remain for ever just where we are.' –
And Mr Discobbolos said,
'Oh! W! X! Y! Z!
It has just come into my head
We shall never go down again,
Dearest Mrs Discobbolos!'

IV

So Mr and Mrs Discobbolos
Stood up and began to sing,
'Far away from hurry and strife
Here we will pass the rest of life,
Ding a dong, ding dong, ding!
We want no knives nor forks nor chairs,
No tables nor carpets nor household cares;
From worry of life we've fled; –
Oh! W! X! Y! Z!
There is no more trouble ahead,
Sorrow or any such thing, –
For Mr and Mrs Discobbolos!'

The Cummerbund: An Indian Poem

I

She sate upon her Dobie,
To watch the Evening Star,
And all the Punkahs, as they passed,
Cried, 'My! how fair you are!'
Around her bower, with quivering leaves,
The tall Kamsamahs grew,
And Kitmutgars in wild festoons
Hung down from Tchokis blue.

II

Below her home the river rolled
With soft meloobious sound,
Where golden-finned Chuprassies swam,
In myriads circling round.
Above, on tallest trees remote
Green Ayahs perched alone,
And all night long the Mussak moan'd
Its melancholy tone.

III

And where the purple Nullahs threw
Their branches far and wide, –
And silvery Goreewallahs flew
In silence, side by side, –
The little Bheesties' twittering cry
Rose on the flagrant air,
And oft the angry Jampan howled
Deep in his hateful lair.

IV

She sate upon her Dobie, –
She heard the Nimmak hum, –
When all at once a cry arose, –
'The Cummerbund is come!'
In vain she fled: – with open jaws
The angry monster followed,
And so (before assistance came)
That Lady Fair was swollowed.

V

They sought in vain for even a bone
Respectfully to bury, –
They said, 'Hers was a dreadful fate!'
(And Echo answered, 'Very.')
They nailed her Dobie to the wall,
Where last her form was seen,
And underneath they wrote these words,
In yellow, blue, and green: –

'Beware, ye Fair! Ye Fair, beware!
Nor sit out late at night,
Lest horrid Cummerbunds should come,
And swollow you outright.'

NOTE. – First published in *Times of India*, Bombay, July, 1874.

The Akond of Swat

Who, or why, or which, or *what*, Is the Akond of SWAT?

Is he tall or short, or dark or fair?
Does he sit on a stool or a sofa or chair   or SQUAT,
                                        The Akond of Swat?

Is he wise or foolish, young or old?
Does he drink his soup and his coffee cold   or HOT,
                                        The Akond of Swat?

Does he sing or whistle, jabber or talk,
And when riding abroad does he gallop or walk, or TROT,
                                        The Akond of Swat?

Does he wear a turban, a fez, or a hat?
Does he sleep on a mattress, a bed, or a mat,   or a COT,
                                        The Akond of Swat?

When he writes a copy in round-hand size,
Does he cross his T's and finish his I's   with a DOT,
                                        The Akond of Swat?

Can he write a letter concisely clear
Without a speck or a smudge or smear   or BLOT,
                                        The Akond of Swat?

Do his people like him extremely well?
Or do they, whenever they can, rebel,   or PLOT,
                                        At the Akond of Swat?

If he catches them then, either old or young,
Does he have them chopped in pieces or hung,   or SHOT,
      The Akond of Swat?

Do his people prig in the lanes or park?
Or even at times, when days are dark,   GAROTTE?
      O the Akond of Swat!

Does he study the wants of his own dominion?
Or doesn't he care for public opinion   a JOT,
      The Akond of Swat?

To amuse his mind do his people show him
Pictures, or anyone's last new poem,   or WHAT,
      For the Akond of Swat?

At night if he suddenly screams and wakes,
Do they bring him only a few small cakes, or a LOT,
      For the Akond of Swat?

Does he live on turnips, tea, or tripe?
Does he like his shawl to be marked with a stripe, or a DOT,
      The Akond of Swat?

Does he like to lie on his back in a boat
Like the lady who lived in that isle remote, SHALOTT,
      The Akond of Swat?

Is he quiet, or always making a fuss?
Is his steward a Swiss or a Swede or a Russ   or a SCOT,
                                        The Akond of Swat?

Does he like to sit by the calm blue wave?
Or to sleep and snore in a dark green cave,   or a GROTT,
                                        The Akond of Swat?

Does he drink small beer from a silver jug?
Or a bowl? or a glass? or a cup? or a mug?   or a POT,
                                        The Akond of Swat?

Does he beat his wife with a gold-topped pipe,
When she lets the gooseberries grow too ripe,   or ROT,
                                        The Akond of Swat?

Does he wear a white tie when he dines with friends,
And tie it neat in a bow with ends,   or a KNOT,
                                        The Akond of Swat?

Does he like new cream, and hate mince-pies?
When he looks at the sun does he wink his eyes   or NOT,
                                        The Akond of Swat?

Does he teach his subjects to roast and bake?
Does he sail about on an inland lake,   in a YACHT,
                                        The Akond of Swat?

Someone, or nobody, knows I wot
Who or which or why or what   Is the Akond of Swat!

NOTE. – For the existence of this potentate see Indian newspapers, *passim*. The proper way to read the verses is to make an immense emphasis on the monosyllabic rhymes, which indeed ought to be shouted out by a chorus.

How Pleasant to Know Mr Lear!

How pleasant to know Mr Lear!
Who has written such volumes of stuff!
Some think him ill-tempered and queer,
But a few think him pleasant enough.

His mind is concrete and fastidious,
His nose is remarkably big;
His visage is more or less hideous,
His beard it resembles a wig.

He has ears, and two eyes, and ten fingers,
(Leastways if you reckon two thumbs;)
Long ago he was one of the singers,
But now he is one of the dumbs.

He sits in a beautiful parlor,
With hundreds of books on the wall;
He drinks a great deal of Marsala,
But never gets tipsy at all.

He has many friends, laymen and clerical,
Old Foss is the name of his cat;
His body is perfectly spherical,
He weareth a runcible hat.

When he walks in waterproof white,
The children run after him so!
Calling out, 'He's come out in his night-
gown, that crazy old Englishman, oh!'

He weeps by the side of the ocean,
He weeps on the top of the hill;
He purchases pancakes and lotion,
And chocolate shrimps from the mill.

He reads, but he cannot speak, Spanish,
He cannot abide ginger beer.
Ere the days of his pilgrimage vanish,
How pleasant to know Mr Lear!

Incidents in the Life of my Uncle Arly

I

O! My aged Uncle Arly!
Sitting on a heap of Barley
Thro' the silent hours of night, –
Close beside a leafy thicket: –
On his nose there was a Cricket, –
In his hat a Railway-Ticket; –
(But his shoes were far too tight.)

II

Long ago, in youth, he squander'd
All his goods away, and wander'd
To the Tiniskoop-hills afar.
There on golden sunsets blazing,
Every morning found him gazing, –
Singing – 'Orb! you're quite amazing!
How I wonder what you are!'

III

Like the ancient Medes and Persians,
Always by his own exertions
He subsisted on those hills; –
Whiles, – by teaching children spelling, –
Or at times by merely yelling, –
Or at intervals by selling
'Propter's Nicodemus Pills.'

IV

Later, in his morning rambles
He perceived the moving brambles –
Something square and white disclose; –
'Twas a First-class Railway Ticket;
But, on stooping down to pick it
Off the ground, – a pea-green Cricket
settled on my uncle's Nose.

V

Never – never more, – Oh! never,
Did that Cricket leave him ever, –
Dawn or evening, day or night; –
Clinging as a constant treasure, –
Chirping with a cheerious measure, –
Wholly to my uncle's pleasure
(Though his shoes were far too tight.)

VI

So for three-and-forty winters,
Till his shoes were worn to splinters,
All those hills he wander'd o'er, –
Sometimes silent; – sometimes yelling; –
Till he came to Borley-Melling,
Near his old ancestral dwelling; –
(But his shoes were far too tight.)

VII

On a little heap of Barley
Died my aged uncle Arly,
And they buried him one night; –
Close beside the leafy thicket; –
There, – his hat and Railway-Ticket; –
There, – his ever-faithful Cricket; –
(But his shoes were far too tight.)

Saith the Poet of Nonsense

Saith the Poet of Nonsense
'Thoughts into my head do come
Thick as flies upon a plum.'

The Youthful Cove

In medio Tutorissimus ibis.
'Thou shalt walk in the midst of thy Tutors.'

Once on a time a youthful cove
As was a cheery lad
Lived in a villa by the sea. –
The cove was not so bad;

The dogs and cats, the cows and ass,
The birds in cage or grove
The rabbits, hens, ducks, pony, pigs
All loved that cheery lad.

Seven folks – one female and six male, –
Seized on that youthful cove;
They said – 'To edjukate this chap
Us seven it doth behove.'

The first his parrient was, – who taught
The cove to read and ride,
Latin, and Grammarithemetic,
And lots of things beside.

Says Pa, 'I'll spare no pains or time
Your school hours so to cut,
And sqare and fit, that you will make
No end of progress – but –,'

Says Mrs Grey, – 'I'll teach him French,
Pour parler dans cette pays –
Je cris, qu'il parlera bien,
Même comme un Francais – *Mais* –'

Says Signor Gambinossi, – 'Si;
Progresso si farà,
Lo voglio insegnare qui,
La Lingua mia – *ma* –'

Says Mr Crump, – 'Geology,
And Matthewmatics stiff,
I'll teach the cove, who's sure to go
Ahead like blazes – if –'

Says James, – 'I'll teach him every day
My Nastics; – now and then
To stand upon his 'ed; and make
His mussels harder, – *when* –'

Says Signor Blanchi, ' – Lascia far; –
La musica da me,
Ben insegnata gli sarà; –
Farà progresso, – *se* –'

Says Edward Lear, – 'I'll make him draw
A Palace, or a hut,
Trees, mountains, rivers, cities, plains,
And prapps to paint them, – *but* –'

So all these seven joined hands and sang
This chorus by the sea; –
'O! Ven his edjukation's done,
Vy! Vot a cove he'll be!'

When Grand Old Men Persist in Folly

When 'grand old men' persist in folly
In slaughtering men and chopping trees,
What art can soothe the melancholy
Of those whom futile 'statesmen' teaze?

The only way their wrath to cover
To let mankind know who's to blame-o –
Is first to rush by train to Dover
And then straight onward to Sanremo.

The Children of the Owl and the Pussy-cat[*]

Our mother was the Pussy-cat, our father was the Owl,
And so we're partly little beasts and partly little fowl,
The brothers of our family have feathers and they hoot,
While all the sisters dress in fur and have long tails to boot.
   We all believe that little mice,
     For food are singularly nice.
Our mother died long years ago. She was a lovely cat
Her tail was 5 feet long, and grey with stripes, but what
     of that?
In Sila forest on the East of fair Calabria's shore
She tumbled from a lofty tree – none ever saw her more.
Our owly father long was ill from sorrow and surprise,
But with the feathers of his tail he wiped his weeping eyes.
And in the hollow of a tree in Sila's inmost maze
We made a happy home and there we pass our obvious
     days.

From Reggian Cosenza many owls about us flit
And bring us worldly news for which we do not care a bit.
We watch the sun each morning rise, beyond Tarento's
     strait;
We go out ----------------- before it gets too late;
And when the evening shades begin to lengthen from the
     trees
----------------- as sure as bees is bees.
We wander up and down the shore -----------------

---

[*] This poem, a sequel to the original The Owl and the Pussy-cat, was unfinished and did not appear in print until 1938, fifty years after Edward Lear's death.

Or tumble over head and heels, but never, never more
Can see the far Gromboolian plains ----------------------

Or weep as we could once have wept o'er many a
      vanished scene:
This is the way our father moans — he is so very green.

Our father still preserves his voice, and when he sees a star
He often sings ------------ to that original guitar.

The pot in which our parents took the honey in their boat,
But all the money has been spent, beside the £5 note.
The owls who come and bring us nows are often ------
Because we take no interest in poltix of the day.

But Ah! (The Landscape Painter Said)

But ah! (the Landscape painter said,)
A brutal fly walks on my head
And my bald skin doth tickle;
And so I stop distracted quite,
(With itching skin for who can write?)
In most disgusting pickle –

His Garden

And this is certain; if so be
You could just now my garden see,
The aspic of my flowers so bright
Would make you shudder with delight.
And if you vos to see my rozziz
As is a boon to all men's nozziz, –
You'd fall upon your back and scream –
'O Lawk! O criky! It's a dream!'

Spots of Greece

Papa once went to Greece,
And there I understand
He saw no end of lovely spots
About that lovely land.
He talks about these spots of Greece
To both Mama and me
Yet spots of Greece upon my dress
They can't abear to see!
I cannot make it out at all –
If ever on my frock
They see the smallest spot of Greece
It gives them quite a shock!
Henceforth, therefore – to please them both
These spots of Greece no more
Shall be upon my frock at all –
Nor on my Pinafore.

It is a Virtue in Ingenuous Youth

It is a virtue in ingenuous youth,
To leave off lying and return to truth,
For well it's known that all religious morals
Are caused by Bass's Ale and South Atlantic Corals.

The Scroobious Pip*

The Scroobious Pip went out one day
When the grass was green, and the sky was grey,
Then all the beasts in the world came round
When the Scroobious Pip sat down on the ground.
The Cat and the Dog and the Kangaroo
The Sheep and the Cow and the Guinea-pig too –
The Wolf he howled, the Horse he neighed
The little Pig squeaked and the Donkey brayed,
And when the Lion began to roar
There never was heard such a noise before,
And every beast he stood on the tip
Of his toes to look a the Scroobious Pip.

At last they said to the Fox – 'By far,
You're the wisest beast! – You know you are!
Go close to Scroobious Pip and say,
Tell us all about yourself we pray! –
For as yet we can't make out in the least
If you're Fish or Insect, or Bird or Beast.'

The Scroobious Pip looked vaguely round
And sang these words with a rumbling sound-
    'Chippetty Flip – Flippetty Chip –
    My only name is the Scroobious Pip.'

The Scroobious Pip from the top of a tree
Saw the distant Jellybolee, –

---

* Left unfinished by Lear in 1872.

And all the birds in the world came there,
Flying in crowds all through the air.
The Vulture and Eagle, the Cock and the Hen
The Ostrich the Turkey the Snipe and the Wren;
The Parrot chattered, the Blackbird sung,
And the owl looked wise but held his tongue,
And when the Peacock began to scream,
The hullabaloo was quite extreme.
And every bird he fluttered the tip
Of his wing as he stared at the Scroobious Pip.

At last they said to the Owl – 'By far,
You're the wisest Bird – you know you are!
Fly close to the Scroobious Pip and say,
"Explain all about yourself we pray! –
For as yet we have neither seen nor heard
If you're Fish or Insect, Beast or Bird!"'

The Scroobious Pip looked gaily round
And sang these words with a chirpy sound –
   'Chippetty Flip – Flippetty Chip –
   My only name is the Scroobious Pip.'

The Scroobious Pip went into the sea
By the beautiful shore of Jellybolee –
All the Fish in the world swam round
With a splashing squashy spluttering sound.
The Sprat, the Herring, the Turbot too
The Shark, the Sole and the Mackerel blue,
The ------ spluttered, the Purpoise puffed
----- Flounder --------------------------------

And when the Whale began to spout –

And every Fish he shook the tip
Of his tail as he gazed on the Scroobious Pip.

At last they said to the whale – 'By far
You're the biggest Fish – you know you are!
Swim close to the Scroobious Pip and say,
"Tell us all about yourself we pray! –
For to know you yourself is our only wish;
Are you Beast or Insect, Bird or Fish?"'

The Scroobious Pip looked softly round
And sung these words with a liquid sound –
   'Pliffity Flip; Pliffety Flip; –
   My only name is the Scroobious Pip.'

The scroobious Pip sate under a tree
By the silent shores of the Jellybolee; –
All the insects in all the world
About the Scroobious Pip entwirled.
Beetles and ------ with purple eyes
Gnats and buzztilential Flies –
Grasshoppers, Butterflies, Spiders too,
Wasps and Bees and Dragon-flies blue,
And when the Gnats began to hum
------ bounced like a dismal drum,
And every insect curled the tip
Of his snout, and looked a the Scroobious Pip.

At last they said to the Ant – 'By far
You're the wisest Insect – you know you are!
Creep close to the Scroobious Pip and say,
"Tell us all about yourself we pray! –
For we can't find out, and we can't tell why –
If you're Beast or Fish or a Bird or a Fly."'

The Scroobious Pip turned quickly round
And sang these words with a whistly sound –
    'Wizzeby wip – wizzeby wip –
    My only name is the Scroobious Pip.'

Then all the Beasts that walk on the ground
Danced in a circle round and round,
And all the Birds that fly in the air
Flew round and round in a circle there,
And all the Fish in the Jellybolee
Swum in a circle about the sea,
And all the Insects that creep or go
Buzzed in a circle to and fro –
And they roared and sang and whistled and cried
Till the noise was heard from side to side –
    'Chippetty tip! Chippetty tip!
    Its only name is the Scroobious Pip.'

Cold are the Crabs

Cold are the crabs that crawl on yonder hills,
Colder the cucumbers that grow beneath,
And colder still the brazen chops that wreathe
The tedious gloom of philosophic pills!
For when the tardy gloom of nectar fills
The simple bowls of demons and of men,
There lurks the feeble mouse, the homely hen,
And there the porcupine with all her quills.
Yet much remains – to weave a solemn strain
That lingering sadly – slowly dies away,
Daily departing with departing day
A pea-green gamut on a distant plain
Where wily walrusses in congress meet –
    Such such is life –

LIMERICKS

There was an Old Man with a beard,
Who said, 'It is just as I feared! –
Two Owls and a Hen,
Four Larks and a Wren,
Have all built their nests in my beard!'

There was a Young Lady of Ryde,
Whose shoe-strings were seldom untied;
She purchased some clogs,
And some small spotty dogs,
And frequently walked about Ryde.

There was an Old Man with a nose,
Who said, 'If you choose to suppose,
That my nose is too long,
You are certainly wrong!'
That remarkable Man with a nose.

There was an Old Man on a hill,
Who seldom, if ever, stood still;
He ran up and down,
In his Grandmother's gown,
Which adorned that Old Man on a hill.

There was a Young Lady whose bonnet,
Came untied when the birds sate upon it;
But she said, 'I don't care!
All the birds in the air
Are welcome to sit on my bonnet!'

There was a Young Person of Smyrna,
Whose Grandmother threatened to burn her;
But she seized on the Cat,
And said, 'Granny, burn that!
You incongruous Old Woman of Smyrna!'

There was an Old Person of Chili,
Whose conduct was painful and silly;
He sate on the stairs,
Eating apples and pears,
That imprudent Old Person of Chili.

There was an Old Man with a gong,
Who bumped at it all the day long;
But they called out, 'O law!
You're a horrid old bore!'
So they smashed that Old Man with a gong.

There was an Old Lady of Chertsey,
Who made a remarkable curtsey;
She twirled round and round,
Till she sunk underground,
Which distressed all the people of Chertsey.

There was an Old Man in a tree,
Who was horribly bored by a Bee;
When they said, 'Does it buzz?'
He replied, 'Yes, it does!
It's a regular brute of a Bee!'

There was an Old Man with a flute,
A sarpint ran into his boot;
But he played day and night,
Till the sarpint took flight,
And avoided that man with a flute.

There was a Young Lady whose chin,
Resembled the point of a pin;
So she had it made sharp,
And purchased a harp,
And played several tunes with her chin.

There was an Old Man of Kilkenny,
Who never had more than a penny;
He spent all that money,
In onions and honey,
That wayward Old Man of Kilkenny.

There was an Old Person of Ischia,
Whose conduct grew friskier and friskier;
He danced hornpipes and jigs,
And ate thousands of figs,
That lively Old Person of Ischia.

There was an Old Man in a boat,
Who said, 'I'm afloat! I'm afloat!'
When they said, 'No! you ain't!'
He was ready to faint,
That unhappy Old Man in a boat.

There was a Young Lady of Portugal,
Whose ideas were excessively nautical;
She climbed up a tree,
To examine the sea,
But declared she would never leave Portugal.

There was an Old Man of Moldavia,
Who had the most curious behaviour;
For while he was able,
He slept on a table,
That funny Old Man of Moldavia

There was an Old Man of Madras,
Who rode on a cream-coloured ass;
But the length of its ears,
So promoted his fears,
That it killed that Old Man of Madras.

There was an Old Person of Leeds,
Whose head was infested with beads;
She sat on a stool,
And ate gooseberry fool,
Which agreed with that person of Leeds.

There was an Old Man of Peru,
Who never knew what he should do;
So he tore off his hair,
And behaved like a bear,
That intrinsic Old Man of Peru.

There was an Old Person of Hurst,
Who drank when he was not athirst;
When they said, 'You'll grow fatter,'
He answered, 'What matter?'
That globular Person of Hurst.

There was a Young Person of Crete,
Whose toilette was far from complete;
She dressed in a sack,
Spickle-speckled with black,
That ombliferous person of Crete.

There was an Old Man of the Isles,
Whose face was pervaded with smiles;
He sung high dum diddle,
And played on the fiddle,
That amiable Man of the Isles.

There was an Old Person of Buda,
Whose conduct grew ruder and ruder;
Till at last, with a hammer,
They silenced his clamour,
By smashing that Person of Buda

There was an Old Man of Columbia,
Who was thirsty, and called out for some beer;
But they brought it quite hot,
In a small copper pot,
Which disgusted that man of Columbia.

There was a Young Lady of Dorking,
Who bought a large bonnet for walking;
But its colour and size,
So bedazzled her eyes,
That she very soon went back to Dorking.

There was an Old Man who supposed,
That the street door was partially closed;
But some very large rats,
Ate his coats and his hats,
While that futile old gentleman dozed.

There was an Old Man of the West,
Who wore a pale plum-coloured vest;
When they said, 'Does it fit?'
He replied, 'Not a bit!'
That uneasy Old Man of the West.

There was an Old Man of the Wrekin,
Whose shoes made a horrible creaking;
But they said, 'Tell us whether,
Your shoes are of leather,
Or of what, you Old Man of the Wrekin?'

There was a Young Lady whose eyes,
Were unique as to colour and size;
When she opened them wide,
People all turned aside,
And started away in surprise.

There was a Young Lady of Norway,
Who casually sat in a doorway;
When the door squeezed her flat,
She exclaimed, 'What of that?'
This courageous Young Lady of Norway.

There was an Old Man of Vienna,
Who lived upon Tincture of Senna;
When that did not agree,
He took Camomile Tea,
That nasty Old Man of Vienna.

There was an Old Person whose habits,
Induced him to feed upon Rabbits;
When he'd eaten eighteen,
He turned perfectly green,
Upon which he relinquished those habits.

There was an Old Person of Dover,
Who rushed through a field of blue Clover;
But some very large bees,
Stung his nose and his knees,
So he very soon went back to Dover.

There was an Old Man of Marseilles,
Whose daughters wore bottle-green veils;
They caught several fish,
Which they put in a dish,
And sent to their Pa' at Marseilles.

There was an Old Person of Cadiz,
Who was always polite to all ladies;
But in handing his daughter,
He fell into the water,
Which drowned that Old Person of Cadiz.

There was an Old Person of Basing,
Whose presence of mind was amazing;
He purchased a steed,
Which he rode at full speed,
And escaped from the people of Basing.

There was an Old Man of Quebec,
A beetle ran over his neck;
But he cried, 'With a needle,
I'll slay you, O beadle!'
That angry Old Man of Quebec.

There was an Old Person of Philae,
Whose conduct was scroobious and wily;
He rushed up a Palm,
When the weather was calm,
And observed all the ruins of Philae.

There was a Young Lady of Bute,
Who played on a silver-gilt flute;
She played several jigs,
To her uncle's white pigs,
That amusing Young Lady of Bute.

There was a Young Lady whose nose,
Was so long that it reached to her toes;
So she hired an Old Lady,
Whose conduct was steady,
To carry that wonderful nose.

There was a Young Lady of Turkey,
Who wept when the weather was murky;
When the day turned out fine,
She ceased to repine,
That capricious Young Lady of Turkey.

There was an Old Man of Apulia,
Whose conduct was very peculiar;
He fed twenty sons,
Upon nothing but buns,
That whimsical Man of Apulia.

There was an Old Man with a poker,
Who painted his face with red okre;
When they said, 'You're a Guy!'
He made no reply,
But knocked them all down with his poker.

There was an Old Person of Prague,
Who was suddenly seized with the plague;
But they gave him some butter,
Which caused him to mutter,
And cured that Old Person of Prague.

There was an Old Man of the North,
Who fell into a basin of broth;
But a laudable cook,
Fished him out with a hook,
Which saved that Old Man of the North.

There was a Young Lady of Poole,
Whose soup was excessively cool;
So she put it to boil,
By the aid of some oil,
That ingenious Young Lady of Poole.

There was an Old Person of Mold,
Who shrank from sensations of cold;
So he purchased some muffs,
Some furs and some fluffs,
And wrapped himself from the cold.

There was an Old Man of Nepaul,
From his horse had a terrible fall;
But, though split quite in two,
By some very strong glue,
They mended that Man of Nepaul.

There was an Old Man of th' Abruzzi,
So blind that he couldn't his foot see;
When they said, 'That's your toe,'
He replied, 'Is it so?'
That doubtful Old Man of th' Abruzzi.

There was an Old Person of Rhodes,
Who strongly objected to toads;
He paid several cousins,
To catch them by dozens,
That futile Old Person of Rhodes.

There was an Old Man of Peru,
Who watched his wife making a stew;
But once by mistake,
In a stove she did bake,
That unfortunate Man of Peru.

There was an Old Man of Melrose,
Who walked on the tips of his toes;
But they said, 'It ain't pleasant,
To see you at present,
You stupid Old Man of Melrose.'

There was a Young Lady of Lucca,
Whose lovers completely forsook her;
She ran up a tree,
And said, 'Fiddle-de-dee!'
Which embarrassed the people of Lucca.

There was an Old Man of Bohemia,
Whose daughter was christened Euphemia;
Till one day, to his grief,
She married a thief,
Which grieved that Old Man of Bohemia.

There was an Old Man of Vesuvius,
Who studied the works of Vitruvius;
When the flames burnt his book,
To drinking he took,
That morbid Old Man of Vesuvius.

There was an Old Man of Cape Horn,
Who wished he had never been born;
So he sat on a chair,
Till he died of despair,
That dolorous Man of Cape Horn.

There was an Old Lady whose folly,
Induced her to sit in a holly;
Whereon by a thorn,
Her dress being torn,
She quickly became melancholy.

There was an Old Man of Corfu,
Who never knew what he should do;
So he rushed up and down,
Till the sun made him brown,
That bewildered Old Man of Corfu.

There was an Old Man of the South,
Who had an immoderate mouth;
But in swallowing a dish,
That was quite full of fish,
He was choked, that Old Man of the South.

There was an Old Man of the Nile,
Who sharpened his nails with a file;
Till he cut off his thumbs,
And said calmly, 'This comes –
Of sharpening one's nails with a file!'

There was an Old Person of Rheims,
Who was troubled with horrible dreams;
So, to keep him awake,
They fed him with cake,
Which amused that Old Person of Rheims.

There was an Old Person of Cromer,
Who stood on one leg to read Homer;
When he found he grew stiff,
He jumped over the cliff,
Which concluded that Person of Cromer.

There was an Old Person of Troy,
Whose drink was warm brandy and soy;
Which he took with a spoon,
By the light of the moon,
In sight of the city of Troy.

There was an Old Man of the Dee,
Who was sadly annoyed by a flea;
When he said, 'I will scratch it,'
They gave him a hatchet,
Which grieved that Old Man of the Dee.

There was an Old Man of Dundee,
Who frequented the top of a tree;
When disturbed by the crows,
He abruptly arose,
And exclaimed, 'I'll return to Dundee.'

There was an Old Person of Tring,
Who embellished his nose with a ring;
He gazed at the moon,
Every evening in June,
That ecstatic Old Person of Tring.

There was an Old Man on some rocks,
Who shut his wife up in a box;
When she said, 'Let me out,'
He exclaimed, 'Without doubt,
You will pass all your life in that box.'

There was an Old Man of Coblenz,
The length of whose legs was immense;
He went with one prance,
From Turkey to France,
That surprising Old Man of Coblenz.

There was an Old Man of Calcutta,
Who perpetually ate bread and butter;
Till a great bit of muffin,
On which he was stuffing,
Choked that horrid Old Man of Calcutta.

There was an Old Man in a pew,
Whose waistcoat was spotted with blue;
But he tore it in pieces,
To give to his nieces, –
That cheerful Old Man in a pew.

There was an Old Man who said, 'How, –
Shall I flee from this horrible Cow?
I will sit on this stile,
And continue to smile,
Which may soften the heart of that Cow.'

There was a Young Lady of Hull,
Who was chased by a virulent Bull;
But she seized on a spade,
And called out – 'Who's afraid!'
Which distracted that virulent Bull.

There was an Old Man of Whitehaven,
Who danced a quadrille with a Raven;
But they said – 'It's absurd,
To encourage this bird!'
So they smashed that Old Man of Whitehaven.

There was an Old Man of Leghorn,
The smallest as ever was born;
But quickly snapped up he,
Was once by a puppy,
Who devoured that Old Man of Leghorn.

There was an Old Man of the Hague,
Whose ideas were excessively vague;
He built a balloon,
To examine the moon,
That deluded Old Man of the Hague.

There was an Old Man of Jamaica,
Who suddenly married a Quaker;
But she cried out – 'O lack!
I have married a black!'
Which distressed that Old Man of Jamaica.

There was an Old Person of Dutton,
Whose head was so small as a button;
So to make it look big,
He purchased a wig,
And rapidly rushed about Dutton.

There was a Young Lady of Tyre,
Who swept the loud chords of a lyre;
At the sound of each sweep,
She enraptured the deep,
And enchanted the city of Tyre.

There was an Old Man who said, 'Hush!
I perceive a young bird in this bush!'
When they said – 'Is it small?'
He replied – 'Not at all!
It is four times as big as the bush!'

There was an Old Man of the East,
Who gave all his children a feast;
But they all ate so much,
And their conduct was such,
That it killed that Old Man of the East.

There was an Old Man of Kamschatka,
Who possessed a remarkably fat cur,
His gait and his waddle,
Were held as a model,
To all the fat dogs in Kamschatka.

There was an Old Man of the Coast,
Who placidly sat on a post;
But when it was cold,
He relinquished his hold,
And called for some hot buttered toast.

There was an Old Person of Bangor,
Whose face was distorted with anger;
He tore off his boots,
And subsisted on roots,
That borascible person of Bangor.

There was an Old Man with a beard,
Who sat on a horse when he reared;
But they said, 'Never mind!
You will fall off behind,
You propitious Old Man with a beard!'

There was an Old Man of the West,
Who never could get any rest;
So they set him to spin,
On his nose and his chin,
Which cured that Old Man of the West.

There was an Old Person of Anerley,
Whose conduct was strange and unmannerly;
He rushed down the Strand,
With a Pig in each hand,
But returned in the evening to Anerley.

There was a Young Lady of Troy,
Whom several large flies did annoy;
Some she killed with a thump,
Some she drowned at the pump,
And some she took with her to Troy.

There was an Old Man of Berlin,
Whose form was uncommonly thin;
Till he once, by mistake,
Was mixed up in a cake,
So they baked that Old Man of Berlin.

There was an Old Person of Spain,
Who hated all trouble and pain;
So he sate on a chair,
With his feet in the air,
That umbrageous Old Person of Spain.

There was a Young Lady of Russia,
Who screamed so that no one could hush her;
Her screams were extreme,
No one heard such a scream,
As was screamed by that Lady of Russia.

There was an Old Man, who said, 'Well!
Will *nobody* answer this bell?
I have pulled day and night,
Till my hair has grown white,
But nobody answers this bell!'

There was a Young Lady of Wales,
Who caught a large fish without scales;
When she lifted her hook,
She exclaimed, 'Only look!'
That ecstatic Young Lady of Wales.

There was an Old Person of Cheadle,
Was put in the stocks by the beadle;
For stealing some pigs,
Some coats, and some wigs,
That horrible Person of Cheadle.

There was a Young Lady of Welling,
Whose praise all the world was a-telling;
She played on the harp,
And caught several carp,
That accomplished Young Lady of Welling.

There was an Old Person of Tartary,
Who divided his jugular artery;
But he screeched to his wife,
And she said, 'Oh, my life!
Your death will be felt by all Tartary!'

There was an Old Person of Chester,
Whom several small children did pester;
They threw some large stones,
Which broke most of his bones,
And displeased that Old Person of Chester.

There was an Old Man with an owl,
Who continued to bother and howl;
He sate on a rail,
And imbibed bitter ale,
Which refreshed that Old Man and his owl.

There was an Old Person of Gretna,
Who rushed down the crater of Etna;
When they said, 'Is it hot?'
He replied, 'No, it's not!'
That mendacious Old Person of Gretna.

There was a Young Lady of Sweden,
Who went by the slow train to Weedon;
When they cried, 'Weedon Station!'
She made no observation,
But thought she should go back to Sweden.

There was a Young Girl of Majorca,
Whose aunt was a very fast walker;
She walked seventy miles,
And leaped fifteen stiles,
Which astonished that Girl of Majorca.

There was an Old Man of the Cape,
Who possessed a large Barbary Ape;
Till the Ape one dark night,
Set the house on a light,
Which burned that Old Man of the Cape.

There was an Old Lady of Prague,
Whose language was horribly vague;
When they said, 'Are these caps?'
She answered, 'Perhaps!'
That oracular Lady of Prague.

There was an Old Person of Sparta,
Who had twenty-five sons and one daughter;
He fed them on snails,
And weighed them in scales,
That wonderful person of Sparta.

There was an Old Man at a casement,
Who held up his hands in amazement;
When they said, 'Sir, you'll fall!'
He replied, 'Not at all!'
That incipient Old Man at a casement.

There was an Old Person of Burton,
Whose answers were rather uncertain;
When they said, 'How d'ye do?'
He replied, 'Who are you?'
That distressing Old Person of Burton.

There was an Old Person of Ems,
Who casually fell in the Thames;
And when he was found,
They said he was drowned,
That unlucky Old Person of Ems.

There was an Old Person of Ewell,
Who chiefly subsisted on gruel;
But to make it more nice,
He inserted some mice,
Which refreshed that Old Person of Ewell.

There was a Young Lady of Parma,
Whose conduct grew calmer and calmer;
When they said, 'Are you dumb?'
She merely said, 'Hum!'
That provoking Young Lady of Parma.

There was an Old Man of Aôsta,
Who possessed a large Cow, but he lost her;
But they said, 'Don't you see,
She has rushed up a tree?
You invidious Old Man of Aôsta!'

There was an Old Man, on whose nose,
Most birds of the air could repose;
But they all flew away,
At the closing of day,
Which relieved that Old Man and his nose.

There was a Young Lady of Clare,
Who was sadly pursued by a bear;
When she found she was tired,
She abruptly expired,
That unfortunate Lady of Clare.

There was a Young Person of Bantry,
Who frequently slept in the pantry;
When disturbed by the mice, she appeased them with rice,
That judicious Young Person of Bantry.

There was an Old Man at a Junction,
Whose feelings were wrung with compunction
When they said, 'The Train's gone!' he exclaimed, 'How
    forlorn!'
But remained on the rails of the Junction.

There was an Old Man whose remorse
Induced him to drink Caper Sauce;
For they said, 'If mixed up with some cold claret-cup,
It will certainly soothe your remorse!'

There was an Old Man of Ibreem,
Who suddenly threaten'd to scream;
But they said, 'If you do, we will thump you quite blue,
You disgusting Old Man of Ibreem!'

There was an Old Person of Minety,
Who purchased five hundred and ninety
Large apples and pears, which he threw unawares
At the heads of the people of Minety.

There was an Old Person of Wilts,
Who constantly walked upon stilts;
He wreathed them with lilies and daffy-down-dillies,
That elegant Person of Wilts.

There was an Old Man of Thermopylae,
Who never did anything properly;
But they said, 'If you choose to boil eggs in your shoes,
You shall never remain in Thermopylae.'

There was an Old Person of Grange,
Whose manners were scroobious and strange;
He sailed to St Blubb in a waterproof tub,
That aquatic Old Person of Grange.

There was an Old Person of Deal,
Who in walking used only his heel;
When they said, 'Tell us why?' – he made no reply,
That mysterious Old Person of Deal.

There was an Old Person of Newry,
Whose manners were tinctured with fury;
He tore all the rugs, and broke all the jugs,
Within twenty miles' distance of Newry.

There was an Old Man on the Humber,
Who dined on a cake of Burnt Umber;
When he said, 'It's enough!' – they only said, 'Stuff!
You amazing Old Man on the Humber!'

There was an Old Man of Dumblane,
Who greatly resembled a crane;
But they said, – 'Is it wrong, since your legs are so long,
To request you won't stay in Dumblane?'

There was an Old Man in a barge,
Whose nose was exceedingly large;
But in fishing by night, it supported a light,
Which helped that Old Man in a barge.

There was an Old Man of Port Grigor,
Whose actions were noted for vigour;
He stood on his head, till his waistcoat turned red,
That eclectic Old Man of Port Grigor.

There was an Old Man of Dunrose;
A parrot seized hold of his nose.
When he grew melancholy, they said, 'His name's Polly,'
Which soothed that Old Man of Dunrose.

There was an Old Man of El Hums,
Who lived upon nothing but crumbs,
Which he picked off the ground, with the other birds
    round,
In the roads and the lanes of El Hums.

There was an Old Man of Toulouse
Who purchased a new pair of shoes;
When they asked, 'Are they pleasant?' he said, 'Not at
    present!'
That turbid Old Man of Toulouse.

There was an Old Man of West Dumpet,
Who possessed a large nose like a trumpet;
When he blew it aloud, it astonished the crowd,
And was heard through the whole of West Dumpet.

There was an Old Person of Bree,
Who frequented the depths of the sea;
She nurs'd the small fishes, and washed all the dishes,
And swam back again into Bree.

There was an Old Person of Sark,
Who made an unpleasant remark;
But they said, 'Don't you see what a brute you must be,
You obnoxious Old Person of Sark!'

There was an Old Person of Bromley,
Whose ways were not cheerful or comely;
He sate in the dust, eating spiders and crust,
That unpleasing Old Person of Bromley.

There was an Old Man whose despair
Induced him to purchase a hare:
Whereon one fine day he rode wholly away,
Which partly assuaged his despair.

There was an Old Person of Shields,
Who frequented the vallies and fields;
All the mice and the cats, and the snakes and the rats,
Followed after that Person of Shields.

There was an Old Person of Barnes,
Whose garments were covered with darns;
But they said, 'Without doubt, you will soon wear them
    out,
You luminous Person of Barnes!'

There was an Old Man of Dunluce,
Who went out to sea on a goose:
When he'd gone out a mile, he observ'd with a smile,
'It is time to return to Dunluce.'

There was an Old Person of Nice,
Whose associates were usually Geese;
They walked out together in all sorts of weather,
That affable Person of Nice!

There was an Old Man of Dee-side
Whose hat was exceedingly wide,
But he said, 'Do not fail, if it happened to hail,
To come under my hat at Dee-side!'

There was a Young Lady of Greenwich,
Whose garments were border'd with Spinach;
But a large spotty Calf, bit her shawl quite in half,
Which alarmed that Young Lady of Greenwich.

There was an Old Person in black,
A Grasshopper jumped on his back;
When it chirped in his ear, he was smitten with fear,
That helpless Old Person in black.

There was an Old Person of Cannes,
Who purchased three fowls and a fan;
Those she placed on a stool, and to make them feel cool
She constantly fanned them at Cannes.

There was an Old Man of the Dargle
Who purchased six barrels of Gargle;
For he said, 'I'll sit still, and will roll them downhill,
For the fish in the depths of the Dargle.'

There was an Old Person of Ickley,
Who could not abide to ride quickly;
He rode to Karnak, on a tortoise's back,
That moony Old Person of Ickley.

There was an Old Person of Pinner,
As thin as a lath, if not thinner;
They dressed him in white, and roll'd him up tight,
That elastic Old Person of Pinner.

There was an Old Person of Hyde,
Who walked by the shore with his bride,
Till a Crab who came near fill'd their bosoms with fear,
And they said, 'Would we'd never left Hyde!'

There was an Old Person of China,
Whose daughters were Jiska and Dinah,
Amelia and Fluffy, Olivia and Chuffy,
And all of them settled in China.

There was an Old Person in gray,
Whose feelings were tinged with dismay;
She purchased two parrots, and fed them with carrots,
Which pleased that Old Person in gray.

There was an Old Man in a Marsh,
Whose manners were futile and harsh;
He sate on a log, and sang songs to a frog,
That instructive Old Man in a Marsh.

There was an Old Man of Ancona,
Who found a small dog with no owner,
Which he took up and down all the streets of the town,
That anxious Old Man of Ancona.

There was an Old Person of Brill,
Who purchased a shirt with a frill;
But they said, 'Don't you wish, you mayn't look like a fish,
You obsequious Old Person of Brill?'

There was an Old Person of Sestri,
Who sate himself down in the vestry;
When they said, 'You are wrong!' he merely said 'Bong!'
That repulsive Old Person of Sestri.

There was an Old Person of Wick,
Who said, 'Tick-a-Tick, Tick-a-Tick;
Chickabee, Chickabaw.' And he said nothing more,
That laconic Old Person of Wick.

There was an Old Person of Blythe,
Who cut up his meat with a scythe;
When they said, 'Well! I never!' – he cried,
   'Scythes for ever!'
That lively Old Person of Blythe.

There was an Old Man at a Station,
Who made a promiscuous oration;
But they said, 'Take some snuff! – You have talk'd
   quite enough,
You afflicting Old Man at a Station!'

There was a Young Person of Ayr,
Whose head was remarkably square:
On the top, in fine weather, she wore a gold feather;
Which dazzled the people of Ayr.

There was an Old Man of Three Bridges,
Whose mind was distracted by midges,
He sate on a wheel, eating underdone veal,
Which relieved that Old Man of Three Bridges.

There was an Old Person of Rimini,
Who said, 'Gracious! Goodness! O Gimini!'
When they said, 'Please be still!' she ran down a hill,
And was never more heard of at Rimini.

There was an Old Man of Hong Kong,
Who never did anything wrong;
He lay on his back, with his head in a sack,
That innocuous Old Man of Hong Kong.

There is a Young Lady whose nose,
Continually prospers and grows;
When it grew out of sight, she exclaimed in a fright,
'Oh! Farewell to the end of my nose!'

There was a Young Person in green,
Who seldom was fit to be seen;
She wore a long shawl, over bonnet and all,
Which enveloped that person in green.

There was an Old Person of Ealing,
Who was wholly devoid of good feeling;
He drove a small gig, with three Owls and a Pig,
Which distressed all the people of Ealing.

There was an Old Person of Fife,
Who was greatly disgusted with life;
They sang him a ballad, and fed him on salad,
Which cured that Old Person of Fife.

There was an Old Man of Thames Ditton,
Who called out for something to sit on;
But they brought him a hat, and said, 'Sit upon that,
You abruptious Old Man of Thames Ditton!'

There was an Old Man who screamed out
Whenever they knocked him about;
So they took off his boots, and fed him with fruits,
And continued to knock him about.

There was an Old Person of Bray,
Who sang through the whole of the day
To his ducks and his pigs, whom he fed upon figs,
That valuable Person of Bray.

There was a Young Lady in white,
Who looked out at the depths of the night;
But the birds of the air, filled her heart with despair,
And oppressed that Young Lady in white.

There was a Young Person whose history
Was always considered a mystery;
She sate in a ditch, although no one knew which,
And composed a small treatise on history.

There was an Old Person of Slough,
Who danced at the end of a bough;
But they said, 'If you sneeze, you might damage the trees,
You imprudent Old Person of Slough.'

There was an Old Person of Bow,
Whom nobody happened to know;
So they gave him some soap, and said coldly, 'We hope
You will go back directly to Bow!'

There was an Old Person of Down,
Whose face was adorned with a frown;
When he opened the door, for one minute or more,
He alarmed all the people of Down.

There was an Old Person of Rye,
Who went up to town on a fly;
But they said, 'If you cough, you are safe to fall off!
You abstemious Old Person of Rye!'

There was a Young Person in red,
Who carefully covered her head,
With a bonnet of leather, and three lines of feather,
Besides some long ribands of red.

There was an Old Person of Crowle,
Who lived in the nest of an owl;
When they screamed in the nest, he screamed out with
     the rest,
That depressing Old Person of Crowle.

There was an Old Person of Hove,
Who frequented the depths of a grove;
Where he studied his books, with the wrens and the rooks,
That tranquil Old Person of Hove.

There was an Old Lady of Winchelsea,
Who said, 'If you needle or pin shall see
On the floor of my room, sweep it up with the broom!'
That exhaustive Old Lady of Winchelsea!

There was a Young Person in pink,
Who called out for something to drink;
But they said, 'O my daughter, there's nothing but water!'
Which vexed that Young Person in pink.

There was an Old Man in a tree,
Whose whiskers were lovely to see;
But the birds of the air pluck'd them perfectly bare,
To make themselves nests in that tree.

There was an Old Lady of France,
Who taught little ducklings to dance;
When she said, 'Tick-a-tack!' – they only said, 'Quack!'
Which grieved that Old Lady of France.

There was a Young Lady of Corsica,
Who purchased a little brown saucy-cur
Which she fed upon ham, and hot raspberry jam,
That expensive Young Lady of Corsica.

There was an Old Person of Putney,
Whose food was roast spiders and chutney,
Which he took with his tea, within sight of the sea,
That romantic Old Person of Putney.

There was a Young Lady of Firle,
Whose hair was addicted to curl;
It curled up a tree, and all over the sea,
That expansive Young Lady of Firle.

There was an Old Person of Loo,
Who said, 'What on earth shall I do?'
When they said, 'Go away!' she continued to stay,
That vexatious Old Person of Loo.

There was an Old Person of Stroud,
Who was horribly jammed in a crowd;
Some she slew with a kick, some she scrunched
     with a stick,
That impulsive Old Person of Stroud.

There was an Old Person of Woking,
Whose mind was perverse and provoking;
He sate on a rail, with his head in a pail,
That illusive Old Person of Woking.

There was an Old Man of Boulak,
Who sate on a Crocodile's back;
But they said, 'Towr'ds the night he may probably bite,
Which might vex you, Old Man of Boulak!'

There was an Old Person of Dean
Who dined on one pea, and one bean;
For he said, 'More than that, would make me too fat,'
That cautious Old Person of Dean.

There was an Old Person of Skye,
Who waltz'd with a Bluebottle fly:
They buzz'd a sweet tune, to the light of the moon,
And entranced all the people of Skye.

There was a Young Lady in blue,
Who said, 'Is it you? Is it you?'
When they said, 'Yes, it is,' – she replied only, 'Whizz!'
That ungracious Young Lady in blue.

There was an Old Man of Blackheath,
Whose head was adorned with a wreath
Of lobsters and spice, pickled onions and mice,
That uncommon Old Man of Blackheath.

There was an Old Man in a garden,
Who always begged every one's pardon;
When they asked him, 'What for?' – he replied,
  'You're a bore!
And I trust you'll go out of my garden.'

There was an Old Person of Pisa,
Whose daughters did nothing to please her;
She dressed them in gray, and banged them all day,
Round the walls of the city of Pisa.

There was an Old Man, who when little
Fell casually into a kettle;
But, growing too stout, he could never get out,
So he passed all his life in that kettle.

There was an Old Person of Florence,
Who held mutton chops in abhorrence;
He purchased a Bustard, and fried him in Mustard,
Which choked that Old Person of Florence.

There was an Old Person of Dundalk,
Who tried to teach fishes to walk;
When they tumbled down dead, he grew weary, and said,
'I had better go back to Dundalk!'

There was an Old Person of Sheen,
Whose expression was calm and serene;
He sate in the water, and drank bottled porter,
That placid Old Person of Sheen.

There was an Old Person of Ware,
Who rode on the back of a bear;
When they ask'd, 'Does it trot?' – he said, 'Certainly not!
He's a Moppsikon Floppsikon bear!'

There was an Old Person of Shoreham,
Whose habits were marked by decorum;
He bought an Umbrella, and sate in the cellar,
Which pleased all the people of Shoreham.

There was a Young Person of Janina,
Whose uncle was always a fanning her;
When he fanned off her head, she smiled sweetly, and said,
'You propitious Old Person of Janina!'

There was an Old Person of Bar,
Who passed all her life in a jar,
Which she painted pea-green, to appear more serene,
That placid Old Person of Bar.

There was an Old Man of Cashmere,
Whose movements were scroobious and queer;
Being slender and tall, he looked over a wall,
And perceived two fat ducks of Cashmere.

There was a Young Person of Kew,
Whose virtues and vices were few;
But with blamable haste she devoured some hot paste,
Which destroyed that Young Person of Kew.

There was an Old Person of Cassel,
Whose nose finished off in a tassel;
But they call'd out, 'Oh well! – don't it look like a bell!'
Which perplexed that Old Person of Cassel.

There was an Old Person of Pett,
Who was partly consumed by regret;
He sate in a cart, and ate cold apple tart,
Which relieved that Old Person of Pett.

There was an Old Person of Jodd,
Whose ways were perplexing and odd;
She purchased a whistle, and sate on a thistle,
And squeaked to the people of Jodd.

There was an Old Man of Spithead,
Who opened the window, and said, –
'Fil-jomble, fil-jumble, fil-rumble-come-tumble!'
That doubtful Old Man of Spithead.

There was an Old Person of Bude,
Whose deportment was vicious and crude;
He wore a large ruff of pale straw-colored stuff,
Which perplexed all the people of Bude.

There was an Old Man on the Border,
Who lived in the utmost disorder;
He danced with the cat, and made tea in his hat,
Which vexed all the folks on the Border.

There was an Old Man of Dumbree,
Who taught little owls to drink tea;
For he said, 'To eat mice is not proper or nice,'
That amiable Man of Dumbree.

There was an Old Person of Brigg,
Who purchased no end of a wig;
So that only his nose, and the end of his toes,
Could be seen when he walked about Brigg.

There was an Old Person of Filey,
Of whom his acquaintance spoke highly;
He danced perfectly well, to the sound of a bell,
And delighted the people of Filey.

There was an Old Man of Messina,
Whose daughter was named Opsibeena;
She wore a small wig, and rode out on a pig,
To the perfect delight of Messina.

There was an Old Man who felt pert
When he wore a palerose-coloured shirt.
When they said 'Is it pleasant?'
He cried 'Not at present –
It's a *leetle* too short – is my shirt!'

There was an Old Person of Páxo
Which complained when the fleas bit his back so,
But they gave him a chair
And impelled him to swear,
Which relieved that Old Person of Páxo.

NONSENSE ALPHABETS

A was an ant
Who seldom stood still,
And who made a nice house
In the side of a hill.

a

Nice little ant!

B was a book
With a binding of blue,
And pictures and stories
For me and for you.

b

Nice little book!

C was a cat
Who ran after a rat;
But his courage did fail
When she seized on his tail.

c
Crafty old cat!

D was a duck
With spots on his back,
Who lived in the water,
And always said 'Quack!'

d
Dear little duck!

E was an elephant,
Stately and wise:
He had tusks and a trunk,
And two queer little eyes.

e

Oh, what funny small eyes!

F was a fish
Who was caught in a net;
But he got out again,
And is quite alive yet.

f

Lively young fish!

G was a goat
Who was spotted with brown:
When he did not lie still
He walked up and down.

g

Good little goat!

H was a hat
Which was all on one side;
Its crown was too high,
And its brim was too wide.

h

Oh, what a hat!

I was some ice
So white and so nice,
But which nobody tasted;
And so it was wasted.

i

All that good ice!

J was a jackdaw
Who hopped up and down
In the principal street
Of a neighbouring town.

j

All through the town!

K was a kite
Which flew out of sight,
Above houses so high,
Quite into the sky.

k

Fly away, kite!

L was a light
Which burned all the night,
And lighted the gloom
Of a very dark room.

l

Useful nice light!

M was a mill
Which stood on a hill,
And turned round and round
With a loud hummy sound.

m

Useful old mill!

N was a net
Which was thrown in the sea
To catch fish for dinner
For you and for me.

n

Nice little net!

O was an orange
So yellow and round:
When it fell off the tree,
It fell down to the ground.

O

Down to the ground!

P was a pig,
Who was not very big;
But his tail was too curly,
And that made him surly.

p

Cross little pig!

Q was a quail
With a very short tail;
And he fed upon corn
In the evening and morn.

q

Quaint little quail!

R was a rabbit,
Who had a bad habit
Of eating the flowers
In gardens and bowers.

r

Naughty fat rabbit!

S was the sugar-tongs,
Nippity-nee,
To take up the sugar
To put in our tea.

s

Nippity-nee!

T was a tortoise,
All yellow and black:
He walked slowly away,
And he never came back.

t

Torty never came back!

U was an urn
All polished and bright,
And full of hot water
At noon and at night.

u

Useful old urn!

V was a villa
Which stood on a hill,
By the side of a river,
And close to a mill.

v

Nice little villa!

W was a whale
With a very long tail,
Whose movements were frantic
Across the Atlantic.

W

Monstrous old whale!

X was King Xerxes,
Who, more than all Turks, is
Renowned for his fashion
Of fury and passion.

X

Angry old Xerxes!

Y was a yew,
Which flourished and grew
By a quiet abode
Near the side of a road.

y

Dark little yew!

Z was some zinc,
So shiny and bright,
Which caused you to wink
In the sun's merry light.

Z

Beautiful zinc!

No. 2

a

A was once an apple-pie,
Pidy,
Widy,
Tidy,
Pidy,
Nice insidy,
Apple-pie!

b

B was once a little bear,
Beary,
Wary,
Hairy,
Beary,
Taky cary,
Little bear!

c

C was once a little cake,
Caky,
Baky,
Maky,
Caky,
Taky caky,
Little cake!

d

D was once a little doll,
Dolly,
Molly,
Polly,
Nolly,
Nursy dolly,
Little doll!

e

E was once a little eel,
Eely,
Weely,
Peely,
Eely,
Twirly, tweely,
Little eel!

f

F was once a little fish,
Fishy,
Wishy,
Squishy,
Fishy,
In a dishy,
Little fish!

g

G was once a little goose,
Goosy,
Moosy,
Boosey,
Goosey,
Waddly-woosy,
Little goose!

h

H was once a little hen,
Henny,
Chenny,
Tenny,
Henny.
Eggsy-any,
Little hen?

i

I was once a bottle of ink
Inky,
Dinky,
Thinky,
Inky,
Blacky minky,
Bottle of ink!

j

J was once a jar of jam,
Jammy,
Mammy,
Clammy,
Jammy,
Sweety, swammy,
Jar of jam!

k

K was once a little kite,
Kity,
Whity,
Flighty,
Kity,
Out of sighty,
Little kite!

l

L was once a little lark,
Larky,
Marky,
Harky,
Larky,
In the parky,
Little lark!

m

M was once a little mouse,
Mousy,
Bousy,
Sousy,
Mousy,
In the housy,
Little mouse!

n

N was once a little needle,
Needly,
Tweedly,
Threedly,
Needly,
Wisky, wheedly,
Little needle!

o

O was once a little owl,
Owly,
Prowly,
Howly,
Owly,
Browny fowly,
Little owl!

p

P was once a little pump,
Pumpy,
Slumpy,
Flumpy,
Pumpy,
Dumpy, thumpy,
Little pump!

q

Q was once a little quail,
Quaily,
Faily,
Daily,
Quaily,
Stumpy-taily,
Little quail!

r

R was once a little rose,
Rosy,
Posy,
Nosy,
Rosy,
Blows-y, grows-y,
Little rose!

s

S was once a little shrimp,
Shrimpy,
Nimpy,
Flimpy,
Shrimpy.
Jumpy, jimpy,
Little shrimp!

t

T was once a little thrush,
Thrushy,
Hushy,
Bushy,
Thrushy,
Flitty, flushy,
Little thrush!

u

U was once a little urn,
Urny,
Burny,
Turny,
Urny,
Bubbly, burny,
Little urn!

v

V was once a little vine,
Viny,
Winy,
Twiny,
Viny,
Twisty-twiny,
Little vine!

w

W was once a whale,
Whaly,
Scaly,
Shaly,
Whaly,
Tumbly-taily,
Mighty whale!

X

X was once a great king Xerxes,
Xerxy,
Perxy,
Turxy,
Xerxy,
Linxy, lurxy,
Great King Xerxes!

Y

Y was once a little yew,
Yewdy,
Fewdy,
Crudy,
Yewdy,
Growdy, grewdy,
Little yew!

Z

Z was once a piece of zinc,
Tinky,
Winky,
Blinky,
Tinky,
Tinkly minky,
Piece of zinc!

No. 3

A was an ape,
Who stole some white tape,
And tied up his toes
In four beautiful bows.

a!
Funny old Ape!

B was a bat,
Who slept all the day,
And fluttered about
When the sun went away.

b!
Brown little bat!

C was a camel:
You rode on his hump;
And if you fell off,
You came down such a bump!

c!
What a high camel!

D was a dove,
Who lived in a wood,
With such pretty soft wings,
And so gentle and good!

d!
Dear little Dove!

E was an eagle,
Who sat on the rocks,
And looked down on the fields
And the-far-away flocks.

e!
Beautiful eagle!

F was a fan
Made of beautiful stuff;
And when it was used,
It went puffy-puff-puff!

f!
Nice little fan.

G was a gooseberry,
Perfectly red;
To be made into jam,
And eaten with bread.

g!
Gooseberry red!

H was a heron,
Who stood in a stream:
The length of his neck
And his legs was extreme.

h!
Long-legged Heron!

I was an inkstand,
Which stood on a table,
With a nice pen to write with
When we are able.

i!
Neat little inkstand!

J was a jug,
So pretty and white,
With fresh water in it
At morning and night.

j!
Nice little jug!

K was a kingfisher:
Quickly he flew,
So bright and so pretty! –
Green, purple, and blue.

k!
Kingfisher, blue!

L was a lily,
So white and so sweet!
To see it and smell it
Was quite a nice treat.

l!
Beautiful Lily!

M was a man,
Who walked round and round;
And he wore a long coat
That came down to the ground.

m!
Funny Old Man!

N was a nut
So smooth and so brown!
And when it was ripe,
It fell tumble-dum-down.

n!
Nice little Nut!

O was an oyster,
Who lived in his shell:
If you let him alone,
He felt perfectly well.

o!
Open-mouthed oyster!

P was a polly,
All red, blue, and green, –
The most beautiful polly
That ever was seen.

p!
Poor little Polly!

Q was a quill
Made into a pen;
But I do not know where,
And I cannot say when.

q!
Nice little Quill!

R was a rattlesnake,
Rolled up so tight,
Those who saw him ran quickly,
For fear he should bite.

r!
Rattlesnake bite!

S was a screw
To screw down a box;
And then it was fastened
Without any locks.

s!
Valuable screw!

T was a thimble,
Of silver so bright!
When placed on the finger,
It fitted so tight!

t!
Nice little thimble!

U was an upper-coat,
Woolly and warm,
To wear over all
In the snow or the storm.

u!
What a nice upper-coat!

V was a veil
With a border upon it,
And a ribbon to tie it
All round a pink bonnet.

v!

Pretty green Veil!

W was a watch,
Where, in letters of gold,
The hour of the day
You might always behold.

w!

Beautiful watch!

X was King Xerxes,
Who wore on his head
A mighty large turban,
Green, yellow, and red.

x!

Look at King Xerxes!

Y was a yak,
From the land of Thibet:
Except his white tail,
He was all black as jet.

y!

Look at the Yak!

Z was a zebra,
All striped white and black;
And if he were tame,
You might ride on his back.

z!

Pretty striped Zebra!

No. 4

The Absolutely Abstemious Ass,
who resided in a Barrel, and only lived on
Soda Water and Pickled Cucumbers.

The Bountiful Beetle,
who always carried a Green Umbrella when it didn't rain,
and left it at home when it did.

The Comfortable Confidential Cow,
who sate in her Red Morocco Arm Chair and
toasted her own Bread at the parlour Fire.

The Dolomphious Duck,
who caught Spotted Frogs for her dinner
with a Runcible Spoon.

The Enthusiastic Elephant,
who ferried himself across the water with the
Kitchen Poker and a New pair of Ear-rings.

The Fizzgiggious Fish,
who always walked about upon Stilts,
because he had no legs.

The Good-natured Grey Gull,
who carried the Old Owl, and his Crimson Carpet-bag,
across the river, because he could not swim.

The Hasty Higgeldipiggledy Hen,
who went to market in a Blue Bonnet and Shawl,
and bought a Fish for her Supper.

The Inventive Indian,
who caught a Remarkable Rabbit in a
Stupendous Silver Spoon.

The Judicious Jubilant Jay,
who did up her Back Hair every morning with a Wreath
    of Roses,
Three feathers, and a Gold Pin.

The Kicking Kangaroo,
who wore a Pale Pink Muslin dress
with Blue Spots.

The Lively Learned Lobster,
who mended his own Clothes with
a Needle and Thread.

The Melodious Meritorious Mouse,
who played a Merry Minuet on the
Piano-forte.

The Nutritious Newt,
who purchased a Round Plum-pudding
for his Grand-daughter.

The Obsequious Ornamental Ostrich,
who wore Boots to keep his
feet quite dry.

The Perpendicular Purple Polly,
who read the Newspaper and ate Parsnip Pie
with his Spectacles.

The Queer Querulous Quail,
who smoked a Pipe of Tobacco on the top of
a Tin Tea-kettle.

The Rural Runcible Raven,
who wore a White Wig and flew away
with the Carpet Broom.

The Scroobious Snake,
who always wore a Hat on his Head, for
fear he should bite anybody.

The Tumultuous Tom-tommy Tortoise,
who beat a Drum all day long in the
middle of the Wilderness.

The Umbrageous Umbrella-maker,
whose Face nobody ever saw, because it was
always covered by his Umbrella.

The Visibly Vicious Vulture,
who wrote some Verses to a Veal-cutlet in a
Volume bound in Vellum.

The Worrying Whizzing Wasp,
who stood on a Table, and played sweetly on a
Flute with a Morning Cap.

The Excellent Double-extra XX
imbibing King Xerxes, who lived a
long while ago.

The Yonghy-Bonghy-Bo,
whose Head was ever so much bigger than his
Body, and whose Hat was rather small.

The Zigzag Zealous Zebra,
who carried five Monkeys on his back all
the way to Jellibolee.

No. 5

A was an Area Arch
Where washerwomen sat;
They made a lot of lovely starch
To starch Papa's Cravat.

B was a Bottle blue,
Which was not very small;
Papa he filled it full of beer,
And then he drank it all.

C was Papa's gray Cat,
Who caught a squeaky Mouse;
She pulled him by his twirly tail
All about the house.

D was Papa's white Duck,
Who had a curly tail;
One day it ate a great fat frog,
Besides a leetle snail.

E was a little Egg,
Upon the breakfast table;
Papa came in and ate it up
As fast as he was able.

F was a little Fish.
Cook in the river took it
Papa said, 'Cook! Cook! bring a dish!
And, Cook! be quick and cook it!'

G was Papa's new Gun;
He put it in a box;
And then he went and bought a bun,
And walked about the docks.

H was Papa's new Hat;
He wore it on his head;
Outside it was completely black,
But inside it was red.

I was an Inkstand new,
Papa he likes to use it;
He keeps it in his pocket now,
For fear that he should lose it.

J was some Apple Jam,
Of which Papa ate part;
But all the rest he took away
And stuffed into a tart.

K was a great new Kite;
Papa he saw it fly
Above a thousand chimney pots,
And all about the sky.

L was a fine new Lamp;
But when the wick was lit,
Papa he said, 'This light ain't good!
I cannot read a bit!'

M was a dish of mince;
It looked so good to eat!
Papa, he quickly ate it up,
And said, 'This is a treat!'

N was a Nut that grew
High up upon a tree;
Papa, who could not reach it, said,
'That's much too high for me!'

O was an Owl who flew
All in the dark away,
Papa said, 'What an owl you are!
Why don't you fly by day?'

P was a little Pig,
Went out to take a walk;
Papa he said, 'If Piggy dead,
He'd all turn into pork!'

Q was a Quince that hung
Upon a garden tree;
Papa he brought it with him home,
And ate it with his tea.

R was a Railway Rug
Extremely large and warm;
Papa he wrapped it round his head,
In a most dreadful storm.

S was Papa's new Stick,
Papa's new thumping Stick,
To thump extremely wicked boys,
Because it was so thick.

T was a tumbler full
Of punch all hot and good;
Papa he drank it up, when in
The middle of a wood.

U was a silver urn,
Full of hot scalding water;
Papa said, 'If that Urn were mine,
I'd give it to my daughter!'

V was a Villain; once
He stole a piece of beef.
Papa he said, 'Oh, dreadful man!
That Villain is a thief!'

W was a Watch of Gold:
It told the time of day,
So that Papa knew when to come,
And when to go away.

X was King Xerxes, whom
Papa much wished to know;
But this he could not do, because
Xerxes died long ago.

Y was a Youth, who kicked
And screamed and cried like mad;
Papa he said, 'Your conduct is
Abominably bad!'

Z was a Zebra striped
And streaked with lines of black;
Papa said once, he thought he'd like
A ride upon his back.

No. 6

A tumbled down, and hurt his Arm, against a bit of wood.

B said. 'My Boy, O! do not cry; it cannot do you good!'

C said, 'A Cup of Coffee hot can't do you any harm.'

D said, 'A Doctor should be fetched, and he would cure the arm.'

E said, 'An Egg beat up with milk would quickly make him well.'

F said, 'A Fish, if broiled, might cure, if only by the smell.'

G said, 'Green Gooseberry fool, the best of cures I hold.'

H said, 'His Hat should be kept on, to keep him from the cold.'

I said, 'Some Ice upon his head will make him better soon.'

J said, 'Some Jam, if spread on bread, or given in a spoon!'

K said, 'A Kangaroo is here, – this picture let him see.'

L said, 'A Lamp pray keep alight, to make some barley tea.'

M said, 'A Mulberry or two might give him satisfaction.'

N said, 'Some Nuts, if rolled about, might be a slight attraction.'

O said, 'An Owl might make him laugh, if only it would wink.'

P said, 'Some Poetry might be read aloud, to make him think.'

Q said, 'A Quince I recommend, – a Quince, or else a Quail.'

R said, 'Some Rats might make him move, if fastened by their tail.'

S said, 'A Song should now be sung, in hopes to make him laugh!'

T said, 'A Turnip might avail, if sliced or cut in half!'

U said, 'An Urn, with water hot, place underneath his chin!'

V said, 'I'll stand upon a chair, and play a Violin!'

W said, 'Some Whisky-Whizzgigs fetch, some marbles
and a ball!'

X said, 'Some double XX ale would be the best of all!'

Y said, 'Some Yeast mixed up with salt would make a
perfect plaster!'

Z said, 'Here is a box of Zinc! Get in, my little master!
We'll shut you up! We'll nail you down! We will, my
little master!
We think we've all heard quite enough of this your sad
disaster!'

INDEX OF FIRST LINES